The
Samuel Milton Jones
Papers...

An Inventory to the Microfilm Edition

Morgan J. Barclay
Jean W. Strong
Toledo-Lucas County Public Library

OHIO HISTORICAL SOCIETY
Thomas H. Smith, Ph.D., Director
Columbus, Ohio
1978

ISBN 87758-010-3
LC 78-60485

Published by the Ohio Historical Society with a grant from the National Historical Publications and Records Commission.

Contents

Foreword

Between the mid-1890s and the First World War, a group of reform mayors, who assumed power in a number of American cities, shaped the tone and character of the period's politics and government. Their administrations were part of an era of political, social, and economic ferment which historians more from convenience than accuracy have labelled the Progressive movement. It was as a representative of this concerted effort to reorder and change society that Samuel M. "Golden Rule" Jones achieved general historical significance. The urban progressivism that Jones epitomized was one of the most important phases of the movement. Much of the impetus for national progressivism came from the cities; in a sense the movement began there. And it can be argued that it was in the cities that the Progressive movement realized its most significant and lasting changes.

The genesis of the urban reform movement with which Jones is identified lay in long-standing efforts to overthrow the boss-machine governments that had entrenched themselves in American cities after the Civil War. There were many reasons for this opposition to the bosses, reasons that often had little to do with reform. Moralists, Protestant clergymen, and the "better elements" objected to the ties between city government and prostitution or the illegal liquor traffic. When the corruption of such infamous machines as the Tweed Ring of New York or later Boss Ed Butler's St. Louis gang was exposed, more responsible citizens were appalled. High taxes and the high costs of doing business under boss government disturbed the affluent. Crusading journalists called muckrakers drew attention to wide-spread municipal corruption; Lincoln Steffens' work from this era, The Shame of Cities, proved one of the more influential books in the history of American letters. Although reformers portrayed their battles against the bosses as part of a war between honest men dedicated to democracy and corrupt thieves destroying American liberties, the contention was not this simple. Bosses, despite their corruption, often supported social programs advocated by reformers. Many of the reformers were the "mornin' glories" satirized by the minor New York boss George Washington Plunkitt, and they achieved little after they were able to throw the rascals out. Often reformers succeeded in office only to the extent that they adopted the undemocratic and coercive techniques of the machines that had preceded them. Self-styled reformers were frequently little concerned with the welfare and rights of the people which they talked so much about. Instead, they often represented the interests of the wealthy and powerful who wished to substitute order and economy for the expensive and chaotic arrangements to which boss government often led.

Many of the progressive mayors of this period advanced programs in accord with this conservative ideal. They were, to use the term of

Melvin Holli, structural reformers, interested in bringing efficiency and honesty to city government but not in instituting radical changes in the urban social order. Probably this structural emphasis constituted the dominant strain of municipal progressivism. But there were other reform mayors--Hazen Pingree of Detroit, Thomas L. Johnson of Cleveland, and Jones, all figures of celebrity during the period-- who did try with a degree of success to extend municipal democracy and to limit the privileges of wealth and property in the city. Their efforts contributed to tangible improvement in the quality of American city government in the early part of the twentieth century, and they provided inspiration to a generation of future municipal leaders. Jones occupies the first rank of this group of social reformers identified with municipal progressivism. As the following essay by Morgan Barclay indicates, Jones, with his multi-faceted approach to urban problems and his wide-ranging municipal experimentation, was one of the more intriguing and one of the more instructive leaders associated with a critical period of our urban and national history.

Charles N. Glaab
Professor, Department of History
University of Toledo
Toledo, Ohio

Acknowledgments

The printed guide and the microfilm edition of the Samuel Milton Jones collection were produced with the assistance of many persons. Without the help and response of numerous repositories and individuals around the country in searching for Jones materials in their possession, the microfilm edition would have been much less complete. The following organizations and institutions either gave or lent materials from their collections for inclusion in the microfilm and to them the editors express their appreciation:

Allen County Historical Society, Lima, Ohio
Ann Arbor Pioneer High School, Ann Arbor, Michigan
Bentley Historical Library, University of Michigan, Ann Arbor, Michigan
Burton Historical Collection, Detroit Public Library, Detroit, Michigan
William S. Carlson Library, University of Toledo, Toledo, Ohio
Grand Rapids Public Library, Grand Rapids, Michigan
Rutherford B. Hayes Library, Fremont, Ohio
The Horrmann Library, Wagner College, Staten Island, New York
    Edwin Markham Collection
Hyperion Press, Westport, Connecticut
S. M. Jones Company, Toledo, Ohio
Library of Congress, Washington, D. C.
    Brand Whitlock Papers
    Clarence S. Darrow Collection
Lima Public Library, Lima, Ohio
Maumee Valley Historical Society, Maumee, Ohio
Ohio Historical Society, Columbus, Ohio
    Paul Laurence Dunbar Collection
    Washington Gladden Collection
Toledo Blade Library, Toledo, Ohio
Western Reserve Historical Society, Cleveland, Ohio
State Historical Society of Wisconsin, Madison, Wisconsin
    Henry Demarest Lloyd Papers
    Newspaper Collection

Cooperation, materials, and information came also from the following individuals: Mrs. Harold T. (Helen Jones) Allen, Miss Mildred A. Cowell, Aled P. Davies, Dr. Louis R. Effler, Arthur Einhorn, John P. Evans, Ms. Donna J. Fewlas, the late Harvey S. Ford, Mrs. Jerome W. (Patricia Burns) Johnston, Gerald Jones, Mrs. Hugh E. (Zelma Bigley) Jones, the late Mason B. Jones, Mrs. Mason B. (Gertrude Witker) Jones, Mason B. Jones, Jr., the late Cledith I. Logan, Mrs. Helen M. Orcutt, Mrs. Ruth Janette (Ruck) Orkney-Work, Mr. and Mrs. William T. Rathbun, Bernard J. Toth, Mrs. Richard L. (Susan Jones) Wascher.

Too numerous to list here are the many Toledo area citizens who called or wrote, sharing with us their reminiscences of Samuel Milton Jones.

Key administrative support in all phases of the project came from Morgan J. Barclay who served as project director. Equally gratifying was the enthusiastic assistance so willingly given by the staff members of the Local History Department as well as by other departmental staff of the Toledo-Lucas County Public Library. To the able project typists Kathryn Prusakiewicz, June Kutzly, and Mary Beth Slee we express a special thank you; also to Ronnie Dietrick and K. A. Secrest for their cover design idea.

Several staff members of the Ohio Historical Society facilitated this project: James K. Richards, chief of the Publications Division, directed the editing and publication of this guide. Dennis East, Ph.D. and Gary Arnold of the Archives-Manuscripts Division contributed advice and encouragement, as did Director Thomas H. Smith, Ph.D.   The microfilming was done by R. Douglas Ramsey under the supervision of Robert B. Jones, head of the Microfilm Department.

Frank Burke, Fred Shelley, and George Vogt of the National Historical Publications and Records Commission deserve highest thanks for their recognition of the value of making the Jones papers available to scholars. Without their dedication this project could not have seen a beginning or completion.

Jean W. Strong

Biographical Sketch

Samuel Milton Jones was born on August 3, 1846, in a small stone cottage about three miles from the quiet village of Beddgelert in Caernarvonshire, North Wales. Like many Europeans, Hugh and Margaret Jones viewed the United States as a land of economic opportunity and, with the financial aid of neighbors, the family emigrated to America in 1849 or 1850. The trip of thirty days was probably a grueling one for a family with five children: Alice, John, Ellen, Samuel, and Mary. The family landed in New York City and then traveled to Collinsville, West Turin Township, Lewis County, New York, where Hugh and Margaret raised seven children. Hugh Jones, a stone mason, worked in local stone quarries and also became a small tenant farmer in the Black River Valley, an unprosperous area with a declining population.[1]

Having a distaste for farming, young Sam Jones looked for other employment and, at the age of fourteen, worked in a sawmill twelve hours a day. Financial need limited his classroom education to thirty months.[2] Next, Jones spent three summers working on the steamer, "L. R. Lyon." He traveled the Black River between Lyons Falls and Carthage, New York, on this extension of the Erie Canal. On the steamer, Jones learned many mechanical skills which aided him throughout his life. A steamboat captain encouraged Jones to go west to the Pennsylvania oil fields where riches and high wages could be found.

The young man took the advice of his superior and journeyed west. A poor, unworldly but ambitious nineteen-year-old, he arrived in the boom town of Titusville, Pennsylvania, in 1865 with fifteen cents in his pocket.[3] He failed to find a job in Titusville, but gained employment as an oil well pumper in Pithole City. The wells dried up and Jones spent part of the winter of 1866 in a shanty with four companions.[4]

Discouraged, Jones returned home to New York state during the winter of 1866 and worked in railroad construction. After a short time, he returned to the Pennsylvania oil fields and worked as a driller, pumper, tool dresser, and pipe liner. In the summer of 1868 Jones arrived in Pleasantville, Pennsylvania, during an oil boom and secured steady employment. He managed to save a few hundred dollars and began to purchase small oil leases in western Pennsylvania. Jones secured an oil lease on the Shoup farm one-half mile outside of Turkey City where he kept a small bachelor's cabin which he referred to as "The Fort."[5]

I am Very Sincerly your friend

Jones built an addition to "The Fort" and married Alma Bernice Curtiss of Pleasantville on October 20, 1875. The couple lived on the Shoup farm during the first three years of their marriage and Percy C. Jones, a son, was born to them on February 6, 1878. Sam Jones moved from town to town, following the Pennsylvania oil strikes. From 1878 through 1885, the family resided in Duke Center, McKean County, Pennsylvania. A daughter, Eva Belle, was born in August of 1879, and a second son, Paul H., in May of 1884.[6]

Disaster struck the Jones family. Eva Belle, affectionately called "Midgie," died shortly after reaching the age of two, and Alma Jones died suddenly in December 1885, leaving Jones a shattered man. Jones' older sister, Ellen, joined the family shortly after the death of Alma and helped raise the two boys. Sam and Ellen Jones developed a close brother-sister relationship and she became a source of emotional and psychological support to her brother. The loss of his wife continued to plague Jones; in later years he would fondly refer to Alma as the "wife of his youth." During a prolonged state of depression, family members and friends suggested a change in environment and in 1886 the Joneses moved to the newly opened Ohio oil fields in Lima.[7]

The oil producer, now forty years old, drilled the first large oil well in Ohio, named "Tunget." Oil prices, however, continued to decline and oil processors indicated no interest in new oil sources. A small group of independent oil producers met and decided to incorporate. Individual assets were pooled and the Ohio Oil Company came into being on August 1, 1887, capitalized at one million dollars. Sam Jones purchased one hundred shares of stock at $100 per share and was elected to the board of directors.

The Ohio Oil Company extended leases and grew by producing oil with low company overhead. In the spring of 1889, the Standard Oil Company purchased the Ohio Oil Company. Jones sold his interest in the Ohio Oil Company but remained in the Lima area leasing oil wells and improving oil drilling equipment.[8]

During his residence in Lima, Jones continued to broaden his literary, cultural and religious activities. He assisted local clergymen in fund raising for the construction of a Young Men's Christian Association building and served as superintendent of the Trinity Methodist Sunday School. His love for music attracted him to a fellow church member, Helen L. Beach, an accomplished musician, composer and the church organist. The thirty-five year old Lima school teacher came from a pioneer Toledo family. Helen Beach and Sam Jones married in 1892 and settled in Toledo.[9]

In 1892 and 1893, Jones spent time in the Ohio oil fields observing the drilling process and making valuable improvements in oil drilling equipment. In 1894, he secured a patent on iron pumping rods, known as sucker rods. These twenty-five foot rods with a strengthened malleable joint could be used for deep well drilling, unlike older hickory wood rods.

The Jones family. Left to right: Mary Jones Owen and
Ellen M. Jones. Samuel Milton Jones, John H. Jones,
and Daniel E. Jones.

Jones began manufacturing the sucker rods in a small facility in the Ironville section of East Toledo in 1892 or 1893. The firm, called the Acme Sucker Rod Company, moved to an urban location in 1894. The move to the new location provided Jones with his first real exposure to the social, political, and economic problems of nineteenth century urban life. He referred to the experience as his "first awakening." Toledo shared in the national economic depression of the 1890s, and hundreds of men begged for work when the doors of the plant opened. This shocked Jones for he was accustomed to the good wages paid in oil fields.

As a businessman he began to question the effectiveness of the American economic system and he tried to bring about social and economic change. Company outings were instituted to remove unwarranted feelings of class distinction. When men were hired, they were not asked about their habits, morals, health, or religion. Jones noted long lists of employee rules posted on the walls of many business establishments and he decided to enforce only one rule at the Acme Sucker Rod Company, the golden rule. In later years, Jones stated that the implementation of this golden rule policy was his first radical move. By putting this rule into action at his factory, the equality of his fellow man and the teachings of Jesus were applied to everyday living and working. Jones also instituted programs for employees which were uncommon in the early twentieth century. He established paid vacations, insurance programs, a profit-sharing system and a company cafeteria. A park was established next to the factory where children could play. Jones brought guest lecturers to speak at the park on Sunday afternoons.[10]

Toledo in the 1890s was a virtual time fuze of activity. The sleepy town of the 1850s became an industrial center during the post-Civil War years. In 1880 the city's population stood at 50,137; in 1890 the population was 81,434; and by 1900 the city had grown to 131,822 persons. The percentage increase for each of these two decades was over 61 percent. This increase was the greatest of the thirty largest cities in the United States. Many Germans, Poles, Bulgarians and other ethnic peoples flocked to the growing glass, bicycle, and foundry industries. The staggering urban growth created many social, economic, and political demands: streets needed paving; public utilities needed expansion; public transportation required improvements; housing had to be built; jobs had to be found; and taxes had to be raised.[11]

The national economic depression compounded the city's problem of rapid urban growth. A municipal debt of $7 million aggravated property interests within the community. At $40.41 per capita in 1890, Toledo's was the second largest municipal debt within the state.[12] Unskilled labor earned from $.50 to $1.25 per day. Labor organizations sprang up to meet the crises of employment conditions in the 1890s. During that decade, fifty labor unions or auxiliaries existed in Toledo. The stock market crash of May 1893 left many businesses bankrupt; in 1897, Lucas County housed 6,000 paupers.

Toledo faced troubles commonly associated with port cities. Petty crime was widespread with frequent arrests for larceny, drunkenness, prostitution, and liquor violations. In 1894 the Citizens Federation of

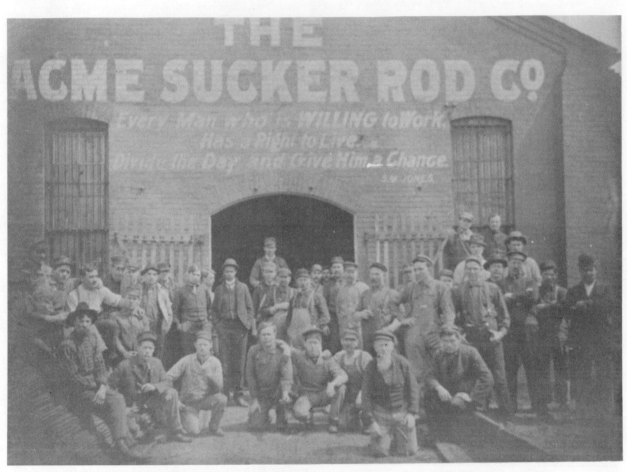

Acme Sucker Rod Company workmen, circa 1902.

Toledo was created as a religious organization to attack gambling, saloons, prostitution, and the lack of enforcement of the Sunday blue laws.[13]

The antiquated structure of municipal government intensified the problems of the rapidly growing city. An 1870 Ohio law created a bicameral legislature for Toledo with a board of aldermen composed of one representative from each ward, and a board of council composed of two members from each ward. By 1894 Toledo had fifteen wards and forty-five council seats. This cumbersome body was further complicated by the addition of fourteen boards and commissions with three to fifteen members each. Six of the boards were popularly elected and all of them acted independently. This large municipal government and its complexity made it difficult to establish responsibility for the performance of municipal services.[14]

The political reality of boss government caused further deterioration of confidence in the city administration. A Republican machine headed by linseed oil magnate Guy G. Major dominated Lucas County politics. Major rose to power with the support of the anti-Catholic American Protective Association. Major also became entangled in the struggle for control of the state Republican party. Marcus Hanna and Joseph Foraker had a continuing battle for control of the party, and Guy Major was a Foraker supporter. An adverse reaction to Major's role in the American Protective Association and his dictatorial rule of the city caused the Republican leadership to look for a different mayoral candidate in the spring of 1897.[15]

The Republican mayoral convention was a chaotic affair. Hanna forces, led by George Waldorf and Walter F. Brown, turned to James Melvin as their candidate, while the "Forakerites" backed Lem P. Harris, a city clerk. A group of independent businessmen advocating "good government" supported John Craig, a Toledo shipbuilder. The convention remained deadlocked through five ballots, although Melvin gained ground; Melvin held 132 votes, Harris 69, and Craig had but 50 votes. The "Forakerites" and Independents realized that they had to move quickly if they were to block the nomination of the Hanna machine. A compromise developed and Samuel M. Jones' name was placed in nomination by James M. Ashley, Jr., son of the famous Ohio Civil War congressman. Ashley gave a strong nominating speech, and pandemonium swept the election floor as Jones received 168 votes and Melvin 103 votes. A political unknown, a successful businessman, and a resident of Toledo for only five years, Jones was definitely a dark horse candidate.[16]

The Democrats nominated Parks Hone, an anti-silver candidate who had come within fifty-eight votes of defeating Major in 1895. The campaign was a grueling one and exposed Jones to the experience of political campaigning. Jones hoped to speak on the issues facing the city such as unemployment, non-partisan government, boss rule, street railroad franchises and municipal socialism. The Democrats, however, cleverly built upon the mayoral candidate's YMCA work, and portrayed Jones as a temperance supporter.[17]

A Sunday afternoon crowd at Golden Rule Park, circa 1900.

Jones spent part of the campaign defending himself against Democratic attacks. In a campaign speech referring to the Sunday blue laws he said that he would administer the law "as will allow to the individual the largest possible degree of liberty for the free exercise of his individual tastes or desires that is consistent with the safety of the city."[18] The mayoral candidate expressed his frustrations concerning the campaign in an address before the Fourteenth Ward Jackson League Club. He noted that Toledo, a city of 125,000 people, faced many important problems as a result of rapid urban growth. Jones observed that the only political issue which surfaced during the campaign was whether or not a few saloons were going to have their back doors open on Sundays.[19]

The mayoral nominee appealed for the utilization of nonpartisan politics in the administration of city affairs. He advocated municipal ownership of public utilities and the adoption of the eight-hour working day. The candidate stressed unemployment as the critical issue facing the city. Jones attacked boss rule of the city and claimed, "I stand here tonight as free as before my nomination, having made no promise of place, position or policy-- not even a janitorship."[20]

Campaigning vigorously, Jones often spoke three times a day. He not only fought off clever attacks from the opposition but also faced internal party problems, for many Republicans actively undermined his campaign. The April 5, 1897, election results gave Jones a margin of only 518 votes or 2 1/2 percent.[21]

Toledo broadened Jones' experiences by electing him mayor and exposing him to urban problems. Lincoln Steffens noted, "The personality of Jones, married to Toledo, developed a further, deeper personality in Toledo."[22] By the conclusion of the mayoral campaign, Jones was known by many reformers; by the conclusion of his first administration, he was considered one of them. Concerned about the economic conditions surrounding him, the mayor consulted the writings of the major reformers of the period, including Edward Bellamy, Henry George, Washington Gladden, George Herron and Henry Lloyd. He drew ideas on reform from the economic and social minds of the period and applied them in unique ways in his city administration. Nonetheless, the greatest impetus upon the man, and thus his politics, came from the humanist writings of Walt Whitman, Henry Thoreau, and Leo Tolstoy.[23]

As mayor, Jones faced an immediate scandal within the police department. John B. Merrell, police board member, preferred a variety of charges against the police chief, Ben Raitz, including drunkenness on duty. When the police board remained deadlocked over the removal of Raitz, Jones was forced to cast the tie-breaking vote and he decided to retain the police chief.[24] In spite of internal conflict, major reforms were instituted within the police department. Civil service rules were established as well as the eight-hour day. The mayor lobbied successfully for the restitution of funding cuts. Jones also substituted canes for clubs on the downtown police beats.[25]

Golden Rule Kindergarten Class, circa 1900.

Unemployment problems continually haunted the newly elected mayor during his first term. Without the modern system of social welfare, the burden of aiding the poor fell to city government and to church-related organizations. Jones reported from a dozen to fifty requests for employment daily. The constant appeals for aid and employment drained the mayor's emotional and psychological energy. In many cases, Jones personally assumed the financial burden of aiding the unemployed.[26]

The mayor realized that many of his accomplishments during his years in office would be intangible. Through his elective office, he hoped to expose people to the progressive ideas which he hoped to implement. Jones stated, "I seem to think of nothing better at present than to use my utmost endeavor, through progressive or radical utterances, if you please, to call the attention of the people to the conditions as they exist around us."[27]

Jones' colorful character and unorthodox ideals made his task of exposing citizens to his ideas of municipal reform an easier undertaking. At an address before the National Association of Letter Carriers he cited the post office as an excellent example of social- istic enterprise carried on by government.[28] Speaking before the League of American Municipalities on August 3, 1898, Jones stated that danger to society and institutions did not come from municipal socialism but from the "lawlessness of capital and the anarchy of corporations."[29] During the winter of 1899, Jones made an extensive east coast speaking tour, including the cities of Boston, Washington, and New York. An address at Cooper Union climaxed the speaking tours; 2,000 persons heard the mayor speak on the subject of municipal ownership.[30]

By the spring of 1899, Jones' reform philosophy was well-known within political circles; consequently the 1899 mayoral election was the most fiery in Toledo's history. Jones approached Walter Brown, chairman of the Republican City Committee, and indicated his desire for a direct primary to choose Republican electorates, rather than a city-wide convention. The party refused and the convention was an unruly affiar. Both Jones and Charles E. Russell, a young real estate dealer, claimed victory for the Republican mayoral nomination. After the first ballot to choose a chairman for the convention, Henry E. King, a Jones supporter, received 126 votes and T. P. Brown held 125 votes. Brown, the temporary chairman, indicated that two delegates did not vote, and that they were required to do so for an absolute majority. After the additional ballot the Russell forces won. Some local news- papers charged that Jones delegates were bribed openly on the conven- tion floor.[31]

Jones refused to take his defeat lightly and an independent cam- paign was organized by his liberal supporters with aid from the Foraker faction of the Republican party. The mayor campaigned on the issue of home rule for the city and municipal ownership of public utilities. Several labor organizations supported Jones, as well as the local police force, liquor interests, and working people. Jones wrote in his autobiography that organized labor and the working man stood against

Samuel M. Jones and Brand Whitlock, a friend and mayor of
Toledo from 1906 to 1913.

"both political machines, the partisan press of the city, and the franchise-hungry corporations."[32] A large candlelight parade concluded the campaign on April 3, 1899. Thousands turned out to march for the mayoral candidate in a driving snowstorm and this event deeply moved the mayor. The victory was an overwhelming one, for the mayor polled 16,773 votes against Russell's 4,266 and Dowling's 3,148. More than 7,000 people cast a vote only for Jones.[33] Jones interpreted the victory as an endorsement of the principles which he stressed: brotherhood, equality, and municipal socialism. The election was the most clear-cut victory of Jones' political career and he often looked back upon this victory in times of frustration and depression.[34]

After the mayor's victory, many Republicans and Democrats joined a "draft Jones for governor" movement. J. Kent Hamilton, former Republican mayor, and A. D. Fassett, former Republican state senator, openly supported Jones. General Isaac R. Sherwood, a Democrat of long standing, thought the party should back Jones as he would receive two-thirds of the Democratic vote anyway. The mayor showed little interest in the campaign in spite of efforts by Republican friends to bring Jones delegates to the nominating convention. The Republicans nominated George K. Nash, a Hanna supporter.[35]

In July 1899, the mayor surprised everyone by accusing the Democrats of holding their convention so late in the year that an independent campaign could not be organized to oppose the Democrats. Jones invited those citizens interested in an independent campaign for governor to write to him for nominating petitions. Within a few days enough signatures were collected to place the mayor's name on the ballot. As a result of the mayor's decision to run as an independent candidate, he lost what remaining support he had with the two major parties and splinter groups such as the Union Reform party.[36]

The Toledo mayor campaigned strenuously in spite of his dark horse status. In a letter to the people of Ohio, he outlined the following platform: abolition of the contract labor system, elimination of prison labor, and state financing of an unemployment program.[37]

Jones focused his campaign upon the elimination of political parties, and he chose to ignore the national issue of imperialism. He campaigned energetically throughout the state, giving 150 speeches in an eight week period, in half of Ohio's eighty-eight counties. He made many friends and won many supporters, as he viewed the campaign as an educational and moral calling rather than a "win or lose" political campaign. George K. Nash, the Republican, received 417,199 votes; John D. McLean, a Democrat, received 368,176 votes; and Jones received 106,721 votes, while other candidates received fewer votes. The results were surprising, for Jones received more votes than any other third-party candidate in the history of the state. The flamboyant orator carried Cuyahoga and Lucas counties.[38]

After the gubernatorial campaign, Jones concentrated his efforts upon the issue of municipal ownership of public utilities. The lighting contract for the city was to expire in 1899 and Jones offered an alternative plan referred to as the Arbuckle-Ryan proposal. The Arbuckle-Ryan firm would build a lighting plant for $250,000, the city would pay $35,000 a year for lighting, and at the end of ten years the city would own the lighting plant. This plan for municipal ownership was put forth in response to the Toledo Traction Company's request for retention of private ownership, but the proposal failed to win council approval.[39]

Another major battle of the mayor's second administration focused upon a natural gas pipeline which was built by the city in the 1890s to connect Toledo with the natural gas fields in the Findlay, Ohio, area. The supply of gas failed and many viewed the pipeline as a financial disaster. Jones expected to turn the failure into success by having the city build a plant to manufacture gas for the city's pipeline. After a yearlong battle with the mayor, city council sold the pipeline to private enterprise. In August 1901, the mayor reluctantly signed a contract for gas with a commercial firm.[40]

As a non-partisan and city administrator, Jones had displayed little interest in presidential politics. The 1900 campaign, however, proved to be an exception, for the mayor felt strongly about the issue of imperialism. Jones viewed the Spanish-American War as an imperialistic venture; therefore, he supported the candidacy of William Jennings Bryan. In fact, the mayor went on a speaking tour on behalf of the Democratic hopeful in the fall of 1900.

The 1901 spring election provided some strange twists: the Democratic party and Negley Cochran, editor of the Toledo News Bee, endorsed the incumbent mayor. The Republicans nominated General William V. McMaken who gathered 9,433 votes to the mayor's 12,576 votes.[42]

In accordance with his annual message of December 1900, Jones advocated the creation of a new city charter. The mayor hoped to streamline the city bureaucracy and thereby create a more efficient system of government whereby citizens could easily affix responsibility for governmental decisions. Jones' proposed charter changes included: expanding the power of the mayor, election of a seven-member city council at large, and the creation of only four departments to be headed by mayoral appointees. In November 1901, the charter was narrowly defeated in the municipal election with 9,505 votes for the proposal and 10,242 votes against the charter changes.[43]

During his last years in office, the mayor concentrated time and energy on the reform of the criminal justice system. As mayor, Jones had the option of serving as police judge in the absence of the regular judge, a custom which the mayor began in 1898. Jones regularly visited with the inmates of the city jail as well as touring other correctional facilities throughout the state.

Jones took his battle for judicial reform beyond the confines of Toledo, for he spoke throughout the state and the nation. In a speech before the League of Ohio Municipalities, Jones indicted society as a whole for the failure of the criminal justice system. Referring to the poor in a speech titled "What is Crime and Who Are the Criminals?", he stated, "They have no money; they have no counsel; and for petty offenses that are not offenses at all when committed by the rich, they are fined, imprisoned, disgraced, and degraded."[44] The mayor noted that arrests for suspicion or loitering were applied only to those in low-income groups. His powerful speech attacking the judicial system was rewritten and repeated on numerous occasions, including addresses before the League of American Municipalities and the State Board of Charities. The mayor disliked the Habitual Criminal Act whereby a person convicted of three felonies automatically was sentenced to life imprisonment; this legislation was repealed in 1902.[45]

When Jones served as police judge he often dismissed cases which he felt were unjust, and in February 1902 he dismissed every case which came before him. These actions infuriated some segments of the community and a bill was introduced to the state legislature removing the mayor's powers to appoint a substitute police judge and also removing the mayor's power on the police board. Under the proposed legislation a police board would be appointed by the governor. Jones said that this law violated the principles of home rule. The legislation passed, but Jones refused to acknowledge the authority of the new police board and fought the decision in the courts. The state supreme court ruled that the special legislation regarding the police board was unconstitutional and the mayor viewed the decision as a victory for home rule.[46]

The mayoral campaign of 1903 was one of the liveliest of the mayor's career. The Republicans nominated a former superintendent of schools, John W. Dowd. Dowd presented many of Jones' ideas but lacked his dynamic personality and zealous conviction. Charles Edson, a bank cashier, was the Democratic nominee. For the first time in his career, Jones campaigned without any newspaper support. Emotions ran high during the campaign and the mayor often spoke two or three times a day. The earlier campaigns had never been calm, but observers noted that this campaign was even more like a revival meeting than earlier ones. Music was provided by the Golden Rule Band and Quartet for the affairs. Jones won easily carrying 10,350 votes; Dowd had 7,491 votes, and Edson gained 4,266 votes.[47]

After his election Jones faced the last major battle of his political career. The traction company desired a twenty-five year extension of the street railway franchise which Jones, a municipal socialist, opposed. The mayor realized that municipal ownership of public utilities was not a viable political position, but he hoped not to extend the current franchise which still had several years to run. Jones hoped a more favorable franchise could be negotiated after the current franchise expired. City council passed the franchise extension and the mayor vetoed the legislation. A public outcry took place as city council prepared to override the mayor's veto. Negley Cochran, editor of the Toledo News Bee, urged a "petition in boots" at council meetings. At one meeting the traction interests were outyelled and Jones was carried out of the meeting by the crowd. At another council session packed with outraged citizens, a traction company lawyer asked Jones if the rowdy crowd indicated the kind of government Toledo had under the golden rule. Jones replied, "No, this is the kind of government we have under the Rule of Gold."[48] The franchise was not extended during the Jones' administration.

The mayor faced increasing health problems during his last years in office. He was bothered by asthma and other recurring illnesses and, after a short illness of three weeks, he died on July 12, 1904. His death at the age of fifty-seven left many of his dreams unrealized. His association with the working people was reflected by the 55,000 persons who viewed his body lying in state and the 5,000 people who attended the funeral of the flamboyant mayor.[49] Reform in Toledo did not end with the death of the mayor; a powerful independent movement soon emerged.

Historians, social science students, and Jones' contemporaries have attempted to analyze Samuel M. Jones' colorful career. Many have chosen to stereotype the mayor and place him within the mainstream of the Progressive movement; others have called him a Christian Socialist. In a written statement in April of 1900, Jones noted that he was called a socialist, collectivist, anarchist, a democrat and many other things. He replied, "I want to avoid any and every distinction that will in any way single me out as being different from the common masses."[50] Herein lies some of the complexity of this charismatic individualist.

Samuel Milton Jones played a vital role in the emergence of the national Progressive movement. His correspondence reflects the interaction of Progressive leaders. Mayor Jones corresponded with Governor Hazen Pingree of Michigan, Mayor Tom Johnson of Cleveland, and Jane Addams of Hull House, Chicago. Jones became acquainted with those who preached the Social Gospel including Josiah Strong and Washington Gladden. The mayor participated in conferences where municipal reform was discussed. He spoke at conferences of the League of American Municipalities and the League of Ohio Municipalities. Jones frequently wrote for the leading reform journals of the period, including Arena, Independent and Outlook. His contributions to the Progressive movement go beyond his insistence upon non-partisanship or municipal ownership. He fought for a more rational, orderly society based upon the equality of men and women and the golden rule. Sam Jones was a dreamer who never lost faith in mankind: a nineteenth century humanist.[51]

FOOTNOTES

1. Harvey S. Ford, "The Life and Times of Golden Rule Jones" (Ph.D. diss., University of Michigan, 1953), pp. 1-6; Samuel M. Jones, *The New Right: A Plea for Fair Play Through a More Just Social Order* (New York: Eastern Book Concern, 1899), pp. 40-42.

2. Jones, *The New Right*, pp. 41-42.

3. Jones, *The New Right*, pp. 42-45; Ford, "Life and Times of Jones," pp. 8-13.

4. Jones, *The New Right*, pp. 45-53; Ford, "Life and Times of Jones," pp. 10-18. ·

5. Jones, *The New Right*, p. 53; Ford, "Life and Times of Jones," pp. 19-20; Isaac N. Pratt to Samuel M. Jones, March 26, 1899, April 22, 1899, and November 2, 1899, Samuel M. Jones Papers, Toledo-Lucas County Public Library, Toledo, Ohio (hereafter cited as Jones Papers).

6. Jones, *The New Right*, pp. 52-56,68; Ford, "Life and Times of Jones," pp. 18-20; U.S. Bureau of the Census, *Tenth Census of the United States, 1880* (Pennsylvania McKean County microfilm roll 1154) (Washington, D.C.: National Archives).

7. Jones, *The New Right*, pp. 54-56; Ford, "Life and Times of Jones," pp. 20-22.

8. Jones, *The New Right*, pp. 56-60; Ford, "Life and Times of Jones," pp. 23-34.

9. Nevin O. Winter, *A History of Northwest Ohio*, 3 vols., (New York: Lewis Publishing Co., 1917), 2:1174-1175; Ford, "Life and Times of Jones," pp. 30-34; Jones, *The New Right*, p. 60.

10. Jones, *The New Right*, pp. 60-65; Ford, "Life and Times of Jones," pp. 45-50.

11. Randolph C. Downes, *Industrial Beginnings*, Lucas County Historical Series, vol. 4, (Toledo, O.: The Historical Society of Northwestern Ohio, 1954), pp. 89-105; U.S. Bureau of the Census, *Abstract of the Twelfth Census of the United States, 1900*, 3rd ed. (Washington, D.C.: Government Printing Office, 1904), pp. 102,105,108.

12. Department of the Interior, Census Office, *Compendium of the Eleventh Census: 1890*, (Washington: Government Printing Office, 1894), pp. 411-412; James H. Rodabaugh, "Samuel M. Jones: Evangel of Equality," *The Historical Society of Northwestern Ohio Quarterly Bulletin*, vol. 15, no. 1 (January 1943), pp. 24-25.

13. Ford, "Life and Times of Jones," pp. 35-45; Rodabaugh, "Evangel of Equality," pp. 24-25; *Annual Statement of the Finances of Toledo, the Mayor's Message and Reports of the Various Municipal Departments for the Year Ending, December 31, 1885*, (Toledo, O.: B. F. Wade Co., 1886), pp. 435-437. The Annual Messages for the years 1890, 1895, and 1900 also reflect many arrests for petty crimes.

14. Ford, "Life and Times of Jones," pp. 41-44.

15. Ford, "Life and Times of Jones," pp. 76-98; Rodabaugh, "Evangel of Equality," pp. 24-26; Hoyt Landon Warner, *Progressivism in Ohio 1897-1917,* (Columbus, O.: Ohio State University Press, 1964), pp. 24-27; Downes, *Industrial Beginnings,* pp. 154-163.

16. Rodabaugh, "Evangel of Equality," pp. 25-26; Ford, "Life and Times of Jones," pp. 98-108; Warner, *Progressivism in Ohio,* pp. 24-26; Downes, *Industrial Beginnings,* pp. 162-163.

17. Warner, *Progressivism in Ohio,* pp. 24-26; Ford, "Life and Times of Jones," pp. 118-121; Rodabaugh, "Evangel of Equality," pp. 26-27; Downes, *Industrial Beginnings,* pp. 164-166.

18. Jones, "Address Before Republican Gathering Concerning the 1897 Mayoral Campaign," Speech, [February-April 4, 1897], Jones Papers.

19. Jones, "National and Municipal Politics: An Address Before the Fourteenth Ward Jackson League Club," Speech, March 23, 1897, Jones Papers.

20. Ibid.

21. Warner, *Progressivism in Ohio,* pp. 26-27; Rodabaugh, "Evangel of Equality," pp. 26-27; Ford, "Life and Times of Jones," pp. 107-141.

22. Lincoln Steffens as cited in Rodabaugh, "Evangel of Equality," pp. 30.

23. Ibid., pp. 20-21, 30-31.

24. Jones to D. M. Fisk, June 2, 1897, Jones Papers.

25. Ford, "Life and Times of Jones," pp. 150-169.

26. Jones to F. W. Holmes, August 28, 1897, Jones Papers; Warner, *Progressivism in Ohio,* pp. 32-33; Brand Whitlock, "Golden Rule Jones," *World's Work,* vol. 8, (September 1904), p. 5310. For the impact of unemployment upon the mayor see Jones Papers, Correspondence, April through December 1897.

27. Jones to Washington Gladden, April 21, 1897, Jones Papers.

28. Ford, "Life and Times of Jones," pp. 184-185.

29. Jones, "Municipal Ownership: An Address Before the League of American Municipalities," Speech, August 3, 1898, Jones Papers.

30. Ford, "Life and Times of Jones," pp. 289-292; *New York Times,* January 17, 1899, p. 3.

31. Ford, "Life and Times of Jones," pp. 310-316.

32. Jones, *The New Right*, p. 112; Ford, "Life and Times of Jones," pp. 321-360.

33. Jones, *The New Right*, p. 112; Ford, "Life and Times of Jones," pp. 358-360.

34. Ford, "Life and Times of Jones," pp. 361-363.

35. Ford, "Life and Times of Jones," pp. 364-383; Rodabaugh, "Evangel of Equality," pp. 37-38.

36. Ford, "Life and Times of Jones," pp. 390-416; Jones, "To the People of Ohio," Printed Materials, July 29, 1899, Jones Papers. The letter expressed the mayor's interest in the governorship.

37. Ford, "Life and Times of Jones," pp. 416-440; Jones, "To the People of Ohio," Printed Materials, [August 26, 1899], Jones Papers.

38. Ford, "Life and Times of Jones," p. 440; Rodabaugh, "Evangel of Equality," p. 38; Warner, *Progressivism in Ohio*, p. 34.

39. Ford, "Life and Times of Jones," pp. 446-455.

40. Ibid., pp. 454-479.

41. Rodabaugh, "Evangel of Equality," pp. 38-39; Ford, "Life and Times of Jones," pp. 506-533.

42. Ford, "Life and Times of Jones," pp. 550-558.

43. Ibid., pp. 559-575.

44. Jones, "What is Crime and Who Are the Criminals?" Speech, February 6, 1902, Jones Papers.

45. Jones, "What is Crime and Who Are the Criminals?" Speech, August 27, 1902, Jones Papers; Ford, "Life and Times of Jones," pp. 578-591.

46. Ford, "Life and Times of Jones," pp. 578-603; Rodabaugh, "Evangel of Equality," p. 39; Jones, "The Police Board Question," Article, May 3, 1902, Jones Papers; Jones, "State Supreme Court Decision Declaring Police Board Legislation Unconstitutional," Speech, June 27, 1902, Jones Papers.

47. Ford, "Life and Times of Jones," pp. 660-676; Rodabaugh, "Evangel of Equality," p. 39.

48. Rodabaugh, "Evangel of Equality," p. 41; Ford, "Life and Times of Jones," pp. 683-690.

49. Ford, "Life and Times of Jones," pp. 729-733; Rodabaugh, "Evangel of Equality," p. 41.

50. Jones, "Socialist or What?" Speech, April 6, 1900, Jones Papers.

51. Ford, "Life and Times of Jones," pp. 735-737.

Chronology

Aug. 3, 1846	Jones born at Ty Mawr, 3 miles from village of Beddgelert, Caernarvonshire, North Wales. Parents were Hugh S. and Margaret J. (Williams) Jones.
1850	Hugh and Margaret Jones and children Mary, John, Alice, Ellen and Samuel emigrated to America. Family settled in Collinsville, W. Turin Twp., Lewis County, New York.
1861-1865	Samuel Jones (age 15-18) worked on steamer "L. R. Lyon" which ran on Black River between Lyons Falls and Carthage, New York.
1864-1865	Went to Pithole City, Pennsylvania, a booming oil town.
1865-1870	Worked in the oil fields of Pennsylvania.
1872-1875	Lived on Shoup Farm outside Turkey City, Richland Twp., Clarion County, Pennsylvania where Jones had an interest in an oil well.
Oct. 20, 1875	Married Alma Bernice Curtiss of Pleasantville, Venango County, Pennsylvania.
1875-1878	Lived on Shoup Farm. President of Turkey City Literary Club. Eldest son, Percy Curtiss Jones born Turkey City, Pennsylvania, Feb. 6, 1878.
1878-1884	Lived Duke Center, McKean County, Pennsylvania. Daughter, Eva Belle Jones born Aug. 10, 1879, died Dec. 19, 1881. Son, Paul Hugh Jones born May 11, 1884.
Dec. 24, 1885	Wife, Alma died Duke Center, Pennsylvania.
1886	Jones moved to Lima, Allen County, Ohio. Drilled Tunget Well, his big strike, 3 miles east of Lima. Met Helen L. Beach, daughter of Mr. and Mrs. William A. Beach of Toledo.
1889	Sold 100 shares of Ohio Oil Co. stock to Standard Oil for $10,000. He was one of 11 directors. Became president of the Geyser Oil Company.
1890-1892	Jones served as superintendent of Trinity Methodist Sunday School and president of Lima YMCA.

1892	Moved to Toledo, married Helen L. Beach on Aug. 24, 1892.
1892-1894	Worked in Ohio oil fields.
May 1894	Patented couplings used in oil drilling equipment.
1894	Started Acme Sucker Rod Co., incorporated 1895, capitalized at $100,000.
1897	Republican nominee for mayor, elected April 5, 1897. Golden Rule Park opened, providing a speaking platform for political and social reformers. Son, Mason Beach Jones born Toledo, Oct. 3, 1897.
Aug. 4, 1898	Speech on municipal ownership given at the League of American Municipalities Convention, Detroit, Michigan.
Nov. 24, 1898	Golden Rule Hall opened, a meeting place for the workmen.
1899	Independent candidate for mayor, elected April 3, 1899 and carried 70 percent of the votes cast.
Mar.-Apr. 1899	Withdrew membership from Westminster Presbyterian Church saying religion influenced by partyism.
May 18, 1899	Delivered speech "Charity or Justice, Which?" before National Convention of Charities and Correction, at Cincinnati.
Aug. 1899	Authored The New Right: A Plea for Fair Play Through a More Just Social Order.
Aug.-Nov. 1899	Ran an Independent campaign for governor. Though defeated, Jones was the first third party candidate in history of state to poll over 100,000 votes. Jones carried Lucas and Cuyahoga counties.
1900	Golden Rule Settlement House and Kindergarten opened. Wrote Letters of Love and Labor, volume 1, a series of weekly letters to his factory workmen.
1901	Elected third term as mayor, April 1, 1901. Wrote Letters of Love and Labor, volume 2.
July 1, 1901	Jones opened Golden Rule Dining Hall and subsidized hot lunches served to the workmen.
Aug. 27, 1902	Delivered speech, "What is Crime and Who Are the Criminals?" before the League of American Municipalities, Grand Rapids, Michigan.
1903	Elected fourth term as mayor April 6, 1903.
July 12, 1904	Died at home, age 57, after 3 week illness.

Note to Researchers

Microfilm Edition:

     The microfilm edition and the accompanying guide to the Samuel M. Jones Papers have been sponsored by the National Historical Publications and Records Commission with supplemental funds furnished by the Toledo-Lucas County Library's regular budget.

     The fifteen rolls of the microfilm edition contain all the Samuel Milton Jones manuscripts held by the library, plus copies of selected correspondence and printed materials supplied by other institutions.

Statistics:

Samuel Milton Jones Papers (Manuscripts Collection No. 2)

     Number of containers: 8 record storage boxes
     Number of linear feet: 10
     Approximate number of items: 15,000

Samuel Milton Jones Papers (Microfilm Edition)

     Number of rolls: 15
     Number of exposures: 17,046
     Average number of exposures per roll: 1,136.4
     Reduction ratio of the microfilm is 15x

Provenance:

     The Samuel Milton Jones Papers were found in the attic of the S. M. Jones Company office in February 1960. Mason B. Jones, the only surviving son of Samuel M. Jones, donated the collection to the Toledo Public Library in 1960. At the request of the family the papers were reviewed by a professor of American history. Eighty-nine volumes of Jones' private library had previously been donated by his widow, Mrs. Helen Beach Jones in 1928; 145 additional volumes were found with the Jones Papers.

     The papers were returned to the library in 1973 and were processed by Jean W. Strong under a grant from the National Historical Publications and Records Commission in 1975 and 1976. The filming was done under the supervision of Robert B. Jones of the Ohio Historical Society.

Editorial Procedures:

The Samuel Milton Jones collection has been divided into the following series:

    Series One: Correspondence
    Series Two: Speeches, articles, and printed materials
    Series Three: Scrapbooks
    Series Four: Pictorial items
    Series Five: Miscellanea
    Series Six: Business correspondence and records

Ten letterbooks of outgoing Jones correspondence begin the microfilm edition and are followed by the incoming letters. Whenever possible, enclosures have been microfilmed with their cover letters. Occasionally, a letter was misfiled in the Jones letterbooks. Researchers may consult the index to correspondents which is microfilmed before each letterbook. Each correspondent index prepared by Jones' secretary contains page references for each correspondent. Researchers may refer to an additional selective correspondent index prepared by the project staff which indexes both incoming and outgoing letters. This second index begins on page 42 of this guide.

Speeches and articles written by Samuel M. Jones appear mainly in typed form. When several revisions of a speech or article exist, the items have been filmed together under the earliest known date. Pamphlets, campaign sheets and campaign newspapers, poetry, and songs written by or concerning the mayor are included within series two. A calendar of speeches and articles appears in the microfilm edition and, also, within this guide.

The scrapbook materials consist mainly of newspaper clippings printed during Jones' political career. The approximately 150 photographs include family portraits and portrayals of Jones' business and reform activities. A fourteen page bibliography listing the works in the Jones personal library has been microfilmed. The business materials primarily concern the manufacturing of oil drilling equipment. A complete index to the business correspondence is maintained at the Toledo-Lucas County Public Library.

Photocopies of materials furnished by other repositories are filmed within the proper series with bibliographic citations added. Approximately one hundred inquiries were sent to institutions and individuals asking for Jones materials. The selection of these possible sources was based upon a review of the Jones correspondence and family history.

Access:

The entire Samuel Milton Jones Collection is open to all researchers. The original manuscript collection and the microfilm edition are available for use in the Local History and Genealogy Department of the Toledo-Lucas County Public Library, 325 Michigan Street, Toledo, Ohio 43624. The microfilm edition of the papers is also available for use at the Ohio Historical Society.

Researchers may secure microfilm on interlibrary loan from the Ohio Historical Society or from the Toledo-Lucas County Public Library. The microfilm edition may be purchased from the Microfilm Department, Ohio Historical Society, I-71 and 17th Avenue, Columbus, Ohio 43211.

Finding Aids:

The published guide to the Jones microfilm edition may be purchased from the Ohio Historical Society. Individual roll descriptions precede each respective roll.

Citation:

Footnotes and bibliographic references should refer to the original collection at the Toledo-Lucas County Public Library and to the researcher's use of the microfilm edition. A suggested form for a first roll citation is:

> Samuel Milton Jones to Hazen S. Pingree, April 21, 1897, Samuel Milton Jones Papers, Toledo-Lucas County Public Library, Toledo, Ohio (Samuel Milton Jones microfilm edition, roll 1, frame 1).

Property Rights:

The property rights to the Samuel M. Jones Papers reside with the Toledo-Lucas County Public Library. The Ohio Historical Society exercises responsibility for the physical custody of the master negative of the microfilm edition. Under no circumstances may a researcher duplicate this microfilm.

Literary Rights:

Literary rights to the Samuel M. Jones Papers have been assigned to the Toledo-Lucas County Public Library. Any questions concerning literary rights should be addressed to the Local History and Genealogy Department, Toledo-Lucas County Public Library, 325 Michigan Street, Toledo, Ohio 43624.

Material from Other Repositories:

In addition to the papers held by the Toledo-Lucas County Public Library, the Samuel Milton Jones microfilm edition includes selected material from a number of repositories throughout the country. Consideration of the requirements of literary rights of material held by other repositories is the responsibility of the author and the publisher. Citations should refer to the repository holding the original material as well as to the microfilm edition.

Series Notes

Introduction:

The Samuel Milton Jones Collection is a rich source of primary materials documenting the development of liberal thought and political action in the United States. Jones' philosophy was a blending of the Social Gospel and Christian Socialism. He championed the rights of laboring people and preached a brotherhood of mankind based upon the evolution of his own social and economic philosophy. The mayor brought a human approach to the mushrooming problems found in rapidly growing early twentieth century urban America.

Series One: Correspondence, 1892-1912 (Rolls 1 through 11)

This series consists of incoming and outgoing letters, third party correspondence, and family letters. Two-thirds of the correspondence consists of carbon copies of outgoing letters, housed in one file folder and ten bound letterbooks, covering the period December 1896 through July 1904. Almost exclusively, the outgoing letters were written from the office of the mayor after April 21, 1897, and typed by his secretary. A few letters were written in Jones' behalf by his son, Percy C. Jones; Helen Lough Wheeler, secretary; Reynold Voit, mayoral clerk; William Cowell, secretary; and W. J. Ghent and John A. L. Dirr who aided the mayor with his publications.

Approximately three thousand incoming letters filed in chronological order focus upon Jones' mayoral years. A comparison of incoming and outgoing letters indicates that Jones failed to keep a large percentage of his incoming mail. Undated letters follow the dated letters and are arranged alphabetically by the surname of the correspondent.

The selected correspondent index, found in the index portion of the guide, primarily contains entries for those persons represented by four or more letters. As some letters in the bound letterbooks of the outgoing correspondence are not in chronological order, the researcher is reminded that each letterbook also has its own index to the letterbook page number. This index, prepared by Jones' secretary, should facilitate the location of misfiled letters and also assist the researcher in finding letters of less frequent correspondents. The index to each letterbook is microfilmed preceding the correspondence. A master index of all Jones correspondence is on file at the Toledo-Lucas County Public Library and researchers are invited to use this card index.

Most of the Jones family correspondence is comprised of Helen Beach Jones' letters. Samuel Jones' letters to various relatives, including his sons, can be found in the letterbooks of outgoing correspondence.

A few pieces of third party correspondence conclude the series; these letters were probably enclosures separated from their covering letters or items personally handed to Jones.

The Jones outgoing correspondence reflects the growing radicalism of the progressive mayor and indicates a wide evolution of his thoughts concerning business, capitalism, urban reform, socialism, cooperatives, labor and social change. Hundreds of interesting and significant letters from men and women representing a wide cross section of American society demonstrate the intensity of the mayor's activity in the Progressive movement and his compassion for the poor urban dweller.

The list of Jones correspondents includes many of the leaders of the Progressive movement, such as contemporary politicians Hazen S. Pingree and Tom L. Johnson. Preachers of the Social Gospel, Josiah Strong, Washington Gladden and Benjamin Fay Mills, also corresponded with Jones. Economist Henry Demarest Lloyd and Edward W. Bemis exchanged letters with the mayor, and Jane Addams and George Hooker of the Hull House social settlement corresponded with him. Labor leaders Samuel Gompers and Eugene V. Debs wrote to Jones, as well as the noted attorney Clarence Darrow. Jones exchanged letters with editors of reform journals such as Munsey's Magazine, Arena, Outlook, and Independent, and journalists William R. Hearst and Lincoln Steffens.

Jones' refusal to identify himself with any particular aspect of the reform movement enabled him to communicate with people representing divergent philosophical views. He participated in reform organizations such as the League of American Municipalities and the League of Ohio Municipalities.

The most revealing series of correspondence includes hundreds of letters exchanged between Jones and N. O. Nelson, a St. Louis industrialist turned reformer. To his ally Nelson, Jones poured out his soul concerning the problems he faced as mayor as well as exchanged philosophical viewpoints concerning mankind.

Series Two: Speeches, Articles, and Printed Materials (Roll 12)

Approximately 210 speeches and articles written by Samuel M. Jones comprise the largest portion of series two. Arranged in chronological order, these writings cover the period 1897 through 1904. Articles are interfiled with the speeches; these materials were published in reform journals such as Arena, Outlook, and Independent. When drafts and published versions of the same or similar speeches exist, the items are grouped together under the earliest known date; undated addresses follow dated materials. The mayor failed to title about one third of his speeches; to these the processor has assigned titles which appear in brackets.

Other significant materials in this series include the thirty-one existing issues of an 1899 weekly reform newspaper, Toledo Saturday Night (later retitled Toledo Non-Partisan and Saturday Night). Jones' annual messages to city council provide a good summary of his urban programs.

The speeches and articles are an invaluable tool for the historian studying the life of Jones. These printed materials show the evolution of the mayor's progressive philosophy, especially his growing radicalism.

A chronological listing of speeches and publications can be found in the index portion of this guide as well as in the microfilm edition of the papers. A topical listing of speeches and printed materials compiled by Jones has also been microfilmed. Jones' compilation is sometimes inaccurate, incomplete, and also lists some items not found with the collection.

Series Three: Scrapbooks (Roll 13)

Scrapbooks focusing upon the mayor's political career comprise the largest portion of series three. The first item in this series is the Samuel Milton Jones Memorial Scrapbook, compiled for Mrs. Helen Beach Jones, containing newspaper articles written mainly at the time of Jones' death. These articles reflect the mayor's national as well as his local reputation as an urban reformer. Telegrams from prominent reformers received at the time of his death are included within this scrapbook.

A second scrapbook of clippings was compiled by the processor of the Jones Papers. Miscellaneous news items found in the collection were arranged chronologically whenever possible; these clippings show out-of-town newspaper coverage of some of the mayor's lectures.

Jones compiled eight small scrapbooks of materials which conclude the series. The first scrapbook in this grouping contains letters written by people the mayor admired such as Hazen S. Pingree, William Dean Howells, and William Jennings Bryan. Other scrapbooks contain newspaper clippings about crime, poetry, and other topics.

Series Four: Pictorial Items (Roll 13)

Approximately 150 photographs from the Jones Collection and copy prints from reform magazines, Jones' published volumes, and newspaper photographs are included in this series. Jones sat for many portraits as photographs were constantly being requested by newspapers and by organizations sponsoring the mayor's speaking engagements.

The images documenting Jones' reform activities are of particular note, including pictures of Golden Rule Park and Playground, Golden Rule House, Golden Rule Dining Hall, and the Acme Sucker Rod facility.

Series Five: Miscellanea (Roll 13)

This series begins with a fourteen page bibliography of works in the Samuel M. Jones personal library. These 235 volumes provide insight into the mayor's philosophy. Many volumes deal with economics, reform, Christian ocialism, literature, philosophy, and physical culture. Jones underlined passages in many of the books and added editorial comments in the margins which provide additional source material concerning the mayor. Campaign buttons, endorsements by local organizations, funeral orations, reform materials and personal memorabilia gathered by the mayor and his family conclude the series.

Series Six: Business Correspondence and Records (Rolls 14 and 15)

This series includes the articles of incorporation of the Samuel M. Jones Company (formerly the Acme Sucker Rod Company) and minutes of the board of directors meetings from January 7 through October 28, 1903. A letterbook of business correspondence covering the period May 19 through September 28, 1903 and pamphlets dealing with the oil business have been microfilmed. An index to this business correspondence may be consulted at the library. Jones signed only a few of the business letters for he devoted most of his time to his mayoral duties. Six volumes of trial balance records (1902-1906) conclude the series.

Roll Notes

ROLL ONE - SERIES I   CORRESPONDENCE, OUTGOING, LETTERBOOK 1 - 2:448
DECEMBER 14, 1896 - JUNE 30, 1898

The mayor answered routine inquiries concerning political appointments, letters of recommendation, and requests for him to speak at reform conferences. With his friends and fellow reformers Jones discussed municipal reform, unemployment, the eight-hour day, saloons, crime, poverty, the work ethic, social settlement activities, and the establishment of a municipal gas plant.

Roll one includes as correspondents: Jane Addams, Asa S. Bushnell, Washington Gladden, George D. Herron, George Hooker, Henry D. Lloyd, Hazen S. Pingree, Josiah Strong, and Graham Taylor.

ROLL TWO - SERIES I   CORRESPONDENCE, OUTGOING, LETTERBOOK 2:449 - 3:695
JULY 1, 1898 - APRIL 17, 1899

Many of the letters concern the mayor's 1899 east coast speaking trip as well as his involvement in the League of American Municipalities. Jones' independent campaign for mayor in the spring of 1899 provides the bulk of the letters. The mayor spoke out on reform issues and his letters also indicate opposition to the Spanish-American War. Jones began writing John Eaton of Pittsburg concerning a patent infringement by Eaton. The exchange of letters continues throughout the correspondence. Other correspondents include: Ernest H. Crosby, B. F. Gilkison, N. O. Nelson, and Eltweed Pomeroy.

ROLL THREE - SERIES I   CORRESPONDENCE, OUTGOING, LETTERBOOK 4 - 5:301
APRIL 17, 1899 - DECEMBER 28, 1899

Several outgoing letters focus upon the mayor's nonpartisan campaign for governor. The correspondence reflects Jones' ongoing interest in municipal reform, direct legislation, initiative, nonpartisan politics, unemployment and municipal socialism. Some letters concern the publication of the mayor's book, The New Right. The impressive list of correspondents includes: Asa S. Bushnell, George Candee, Herbert N. Casson, Eugene V. Debs, Washington Gladden, Samuel Gompers, Henry D. Lloyd, N. O. Nelson, and Hazen S. Pingree.

ROLL FOUR - SERIES I   CORRESPONDENCE, OUTGOING, LETTERBOOK 5 - 6:482
JANUARY 2, 1900 - DECEMBER 28, 1900

The outgoing letters contain the mayor's endorsement of William Jennings Bryan for the presidency. Jones also discussed the renewal of street railroad franchises, nonpartisan politics, unemployment, equality for blacks and other topics of municipal concern. Jones financed the establishment of a municipal lighting plant in Corry, Pennsylvania and the mayor's correspondence with Ernest Hammond is worthy of note. Notable correspondents include: Clarence S. Darrow, George Hooker, Henry D. Lloyd, N. O. Nelson, Hazen S. Pingree, and Josiah Strong.

ROLL FIVE - SERIES I   CORRESPONDENCE, OUTGOING, LETTERBOOK 6:483 - 7:695
JANUARY 3, 1901 - DECEMBER 30, 1901

Portions of the correspondence discuss Jones' third mayoral campaign held in the spring of 1901. Unlike the other letterbooks, many letters written to Ernest Hammond and Percy C. Jones concern business matters. The outgoing letters reflect the mayor's new interest in the physical culture movement as well as a growing distaste for the operation of the criminal justice system. Some correspondents include: Washington Gladden, George D. Herron, Tom L. Johnson, Bernarr MacFadden, N. O. Nelson, and Horace Traubel.

ROLL SIX - SERIES I   CORRESPONDENCE, OUTGOING, LETTERBOOK 8 - 9:216
DECEMBER 31, 1901 - MARCH 30, 1903

The letters continue to indicate the mayor's interest in reform of the criminal justice system as well as his financial support of reform publications. Principal correspondents include: Jane Addams, Herbert S. Bigelow, William J. Bryan, Clarence S. Darrow, Henry D. Lloyd, N. O. Nelson, Bernarr MacFadden, and Harriet Taylor Upton.

ROLL SEVEN - SERIES I   CORRESPONDENCE, OUTGOING, LETTERBOOK 9:217 - 10:509
APRIL 1903 - JULY 13, 1904

Letters focusing upon Jones' fourth mayoral campaign are worthy of note along with Jones' attempt to publish a reform magazine in the spring of 1903.
The mayor continued to comment upon the reforms needed within city government, the criminal justice system, and his desire for the establishment of municipal ownership of public utilities. Outstanding correspondents are: Jane Addams, Clarence S. Darrow, Charles Ferguson, Samuel Gompers, N. O. Nelson, Lincoln Steffens, and Brand Whitlock.

ROLL EIGHT - SERIES I CORRESPONDENCE, INCOMING, DECEMBER 1892 - APRIL 1899

     Many of the initial incoming letters indicate support for Jones'
mayoral campaigns of 1897 and 1899. Speaking requests constantly crossed
the mayor's desk and Jones developed a reputation as a powerful spokesman
for reform causes. Progressive magazines and newspapers badgered Jones
for articles and for permission to reprint his speeches. Many nationally
known reformers including Jane Addams, Washington Gladden, Ernest H.
Crosby, Henry D. Lloyd, George D. Herron, and Hazen S. Pingree corresponded
with the mayor.

ROLL NINE - SERIES I CORRESPONDENCE, INCOMING, MAY 1899 - JULY 1900

     Numerous letters concern Jones' independent campaign for governor in
the fall of 1899. Correspondents also praised and criticized the mayor's
book, The New Right.   Correspondents responded to the mayor's request for
ideas and information regarding the establishment of a municipal gas plant
and other city projects. Outstanding correspondents include: Clarence S.
Darrow, Eugene Debs, Richard T. Ely, John P. Gavit, Henry D. Lloyd, N. O.
Nelson, Josiah Strong, and Graham Taylor.

ROLL TEN - SERIES I CORRESPONDENCE, INCOMING, AUGUST 1900 - JUNE 1902

     A large percentage of the incoming letters for this period includes
speaking and publishing requests. Friends urged Jones to run for Congress
in the fall of 1900. The letters offer differing viewpoints on several
issues, including: social settlement work, taxation, municipal socialism,
socialist colonies, woman's suffrage and capitalism. Jones corresponded
with and financially aided William A. Cocolough, a medical student at
Fisk University, and this exchange of letters reveals the attitudes of an
articulate black student toward early twentieth century America. Other
correspondents include: William J. Bryan, Carrie Chapman Catt, Clarence
S. Darrow, Henry D. Lloyd, N. O. Nelson, and Graham Taylor.

ROLL ELEVEN - SERIES I CORRESPONDENCE, INCOMING JULY 1902 - MARCH 1912

     The incoming letters continue to reflect the growing stature of
Toledo's Progressive mayor. Tom L. Johnson often asked Jones to speak at
his tent meetings and nonpartisan committees throughout the country and
the state Democratic organization asked for the mayor's campaign aid.
     Jones attempted to publish a reform publication in 1903 and the cor-
respondence between Jones and Charles Ferguson is worthy of scrutiny.
Undated letters, family correspondence and third party correspondence
conclude series one. The Jones family correspondence is primarily written
to Helen Beach Jones and includes telegrams of condolence received at the
time of the mayor's death.

ROLL ELEVEN, cont.

Correspondents of note include: Jane Addams, William J. Bryan, Negley D. Cochran, Samuel Gompers, Tom L. Johnson, Bernarr MacFadden, N. O. Nelson, and Lincoln Steffens.

ROLL TWELVE - SERIES II SPEECHES, ARTICLES AND PRINTED MATERIALS

Approximately 210 speeches and articles written by Samuel M. Jones comprise the largest portion of roll twelve. A weekly reform newspaper, The Toledo Saturday Night (later titled Toledo Non-Partisan and Saturday Night) and the mayor's annual messages provide a summary of Jones' urban programs. The complex personality of the mayor and his concern for a wide variety of human and municipal problems are revealed in his lectures and writings.

ROLL THIRTEEN - SERIES III SCRAPBOOKS

Series three contains a Memorial Scrapbook compiled by Helen Lough Wheeler (secretary to the mayor) and a scrapbook of news clippings compiled by the processor of the Jones Papers. Eight small scrapbooks compiled by Jones conclude the series.

SERIES IV PICTORIAL ITEMS

One hundred and fifty images document the personal and reform activities of Samuel M. Jones.

SERIES V MISCELLANEA

This series begins with a fourteen page bibliography of the works in the Jones personal library. Jones underlined and wrote marginal notes in many of the volumes in his library adding to their research value. Campaign buttons, endorsements, funeral orations, reform materials and personal memorabilia conclude the series.

ROLL FOURTEEN - SERIES VI BUSINESS CORRESPONDENCE AND RECORDS

The Articles of Incorporation and the minutes of the Board of Directors (1903--1927) of the Samuel M. Jones Company (formerly the Acme Sucker Rod Co.) are the most important items within the series. A portion of a business correspondence letterbook covering the period from May 19, 1903, through August 15, 1903, is also included.

ROLL FIFTEEN - SERIES VI BUSINESS CORRESPONDENCE AND RECORDS

　　　Business letters for the period August 17, 1903 through September 28, 1903 and six volumes of trial balance records (1902 - 1906) conclude the microfilm edition of the Jones Papers.

Correspondence Index

The correspondence index primarily contains entries for those persons represented by four or more letters written to or by Samuel M. Jones. Entries have been made for less than four letters if the correspondent was a national figure, particularly in the field of urban reform. Routine business letters and requests for speaking engagements have been eliminated from the index.

Three folders of letters conclude the correspondence series and these items have been indicated in the index by the following abbreviations: (ND) for undated material; (FC) for family letters; and (O) for relevant letters not written to or by Jones. An asterisk indicates more than one letter for the given date. The following abbreviations for months have been adopted: Ja, F, Mr, Ap, My, Je, Jl, Ag, S, O, N, and D. The Local History and Genealogy Department, Toledo-Lucas County Public Library holds a complete correspondence index to this collection, and will furnish information about additional correspondents upon request.

Abbot, Willis J.   1901, Ap 2; 1902, Ja 10; 1904, Jl 14 (folder FC)

   Jones to Abbot   1900, S 26; 1901, Ag 6; 1902, Ja 8, 17, My 2, 6, S 24, N 3, 24; 1903, Ap 11, My 20, 27, Je 25, Jl 15, O 15

Abbott, Lawrence F.   1899, F 4, Ap 4

   Jones to Abbott   1899, F 2*, 21; 1902, N 11

Abbott, Leonard D.   1899, Ja 27, O 9; 1901, F 8, D 31; 1902, N 20

   Jones to Abbott   1900, My 18

Acme Supply Co. See also: Maxwell, Frank and Sherwood, W. D.

   Jones to Acme Supply Co.   1901, O 29; 1902, Ja 23, 25, Ap 10, D 1

Adams, F. D.   1899, My 2

   Jones to Adams   1899, My 3, 13, Jl 18, Ag 21

Adams, Frederick U.   1898, Ag 5

    Jones to Adams   1898, Ag 6, 12, O 20, N 2

Addams, Jane   1898, Mr 31, My 20, 28*, O 22; 1899, Ap 4; 1901, Ap 8;
        1903, O 8, 20

    Jones to Addams   1897, Jl 27, N 1, D 29; 1898, F 11, Mr 9, My 25;
        1899, Ja 24, 30, F 1, Jl 22; 1900, Ja 30, O 12; 1902, Mr 31,
        Ap 25, Ag 15; 1903, Ja 29, O 12

Armour [Armor], Robert R.

    Jones to Armour [Armor]   1897, My 4, 26, Je 17, Ag 17, S 10; 1898,
        Ja 13; 1903, Jl 2; 1904, Mr 2

Babcock, O. B.   1902, Je 4, Jl 1, 17, Ag 25, 28, S 16, 22; 1903, F 9

    Jones to Babcock   1902, Je 10, Jl 15, 19, Ag 26, S 17; 1903, F 13

Bacon, (Mr. & Mrs.) R. G.   1901, D 27; 1904, Jl 14 (folder FC)

    Jones to Bacon   1899, O 3; 1903, My 13

Bailey, Jonathan

    Jones to Bailey   1897, My 27, Je 2, Jl 12, D 16

Barr, James H.

    Jones to Barr   1902, Ja 9, F 18, 27; 1903, Mr 9; 1904, Mr 2

Barringer, J. M.

    Jones to Barringer   1899, O 2; 1900, Ag 13, N 19; 1903, S 21,
        O 15, 23

Barringer, Willard   1898, O 10, 17, D 17; 1899, Ap 13, N 12

    Jones to Barringer   1898, O 13, D 20; 1899, Ja 13, N 14; 1900
        S 18

Bartlett, [J. A.]

    Jones to Bartlett   1898, Mr 18, 23, 28; 1899, Ag 21, O 2, 4

Battle, Wallace A   1904, F 6, My 11

    Jones to Battle   1903, Je 25; 1904, F 9, My 13

Bauer, Joseph A.   1899, F 7, 21; 1901, Ja 1; 1902, Ag 12

    Jones to Bauer   1899, F 7, 23

Bell, D.   1904, Ap 10, Jl 13 (folder FC)

Bell, D., cont.

    Jones to Bell   1897, Ap 29, Je 19, Jl 8, Ag 10, 24, S 1, 9, N 2;
        1901, S 24; 1902, Ap 4; 1904, Ap 11, 30

Bemis, Edward W.   1897, O 12; 1899, Ap 7; 1901, Ja 9, D 30; 1904,
       Jl 14 (folder FC)

    Jones to Bemis   1897, O 30, N 18, D 21; 1898, Ag 26, S 2, 14, 24,
       O 13, N 10, 18; 1899, F 24, My 22, Jl 14, Ag 8, D 21; 1900,
       Mr 27, Je 18; 1901, F 12, 19, Ag 17; 1903, S 9

Bennett, Edward   1900, S 24

    Jones to Bennett   1897, My 14, Jl 17; 1899, F 1, 23; 1901, N 12,
       D 20

Bigelow, Herbert S.   1899, My 15; 1901, Ap 2; 1902, Ag 11, 22, O 15,
       D 9

    Jones to Bigelow   1899, Ap 27, Ag 11; 1901, Ap 3; 1902, Ag 15*,
       S 13, 15, 24, O 16, D 10; 1903, O 30

Bigelow, Margaret Doane (Mrs. Herbert S.)   1902, S 16, 23

    Jones to Bigelow   1902, S 1, O 6

Bishop, W. H.

    Jones to Bishop   1897, O 28; 1899, S 7, 18; 1902, S 15

Black, Samuel L.   1898, S 8; 1899, Ap 6

    Jones to Black   1897, S 9; 1898, Mr 10, Ag 23; 1899, My 17

Blanchard, Nellie (Mrs. C. C.)   1898, Ja 10, Mr 8, D 26; 1899, Ap 9

    Jones to Blanchard   1898, Mr 3; 1899, Ja 3, Ap 12, Ag 31

Bliss, Frank L.

    Jones to Bliss   1901, Je 19, 21, N 27, 30, D 4; 1903, Mr 18

Bliss, W. D. P.   1898, Ag 18; 1899, N 8, D 12; 1901, Jl 6

    Jones to Bliss   1898, Ag 23; 1899, F 10, Je 16, Jl 12*, 29, S 27;
       1900, Ja 12, Mr 1, My 26, D 24; 1901, Mr 15

Bogart, John N.   1898, D 13, 17; 1899, Ja 17, Ap 4; 1902, Ag 16

    Jones to Bogart   1898, Mr 1, D 15, 21; 1899, Ap 1

Boley, W. M.

    Jones to Boley   1902, O 28; 1903, F 26, Ap 7, O 15; 1904, Ap 25,
       My 4

Bond, Louise

    <u>Jones to Bond</u>   <u>1897</u>, Ag 5, 12; <u>1898</u>, Jl 28; <u>1899</u>, Ja ..

Bonner, Joseph C.

    <u>Jones to Bonner</u>   <u>1898</u>, Jl 8, Ag 23; <u>1901</u>, Ap 15, 24

Bonsall, Charles   <u>1899</u>, N 8; <u>1902</u>, O 18; <u>1903</u>, Ap 21

    <u>Jones to Bonsall</u>   <u>1900</u>, S 17; <u>1902</u>, O 28; <u>1903</u>, Ap 30

Boyle, P[atrick] C.   <u>1897</u>, O 18; <u>1898</u>, S 19

    <u>Jones to Boyle</u>   <u>1897</u>, O 11, 21; <u>1898</u>, Jl 9, S 16

Bradford, Columbus   <u>1898</u>, Jl 9

    <u>Jones to Bradford</u>   <u>1898</u>, Mr 25, 28, My 5, 13, 24, Je 9, 24, 29,
       Jl 7; <u>1901</u>, Mr 28, Ag 8; <u>1903</u>, My 4; <u>1904</u>, My 11

Brenner, Charles   <u>1903</u>, S 1, 8, 12, O 14

    <u>Jones to Brenner</u>   <u>1903</u>, S 2, 14, O 15, 20, 26

Brigham, Charles G.

    <u>Jones to Brigham</u>   <u>1897</u>, Ap 30, My 24, Je 2, 18

Brigham, Fred W.   <u>1897</u>, D 1; <u>1898</u>, My 18, 19

    <u>Jones to Brigham</u>   <u>1897</u>, Je 19, Ag 9, S 24; <u>1898</u>, Ag 12, O 25,
       N 25; <u>1899</u>, Ja 31; <u>1903</u>, O 28

Brisbane, Arthur   <u>1898</u>, D 17, 28; <u>1899</u>, Mr 9, Ap 4, My 15

    <u>Jones to Brisbane</u>   <u>1898</u>, D 20; <u>1899</u>, Ja 11, Mr 18, My 4, 13,
       Jl 29; <u>1903</u>, Mr 20

Brodsky, Edward

    <u>Jones to Brodsky</u>   <u>1901</u>, F 21; <u>1902</u>, Ja 26, F 7, N 28

Brown, Milton W.   <u>1904</u>, Mr 25, My 8

    <u>Jones to Brown</u>   <u>1904</u>, Mr 23, 26, My 9, Jl 4

Brown, William T.   <u>1899</u>, F 16, Ap 13, Je 13; <u>1900</u>, F 9, Ap 15, 28,
       My 29, D 27; <u>1901</u>, Ja 12, Jl 1, 18, S 23, N 25, D 16; <u>1902</u>, Ja

    <u>Jones to Brown</u>   <u>1899</u>, F 10, Ap 12, 14, Je 17; <u>1900</u>, F 6, Ap 1ʹ
       N 28, D 26; <u>1901</u>, Ja 29, Jl 3, 19, S 24, N 14, 26, D 6; ʹ
       Ap 25, 29, My 31

Bryan, William Jennings   <u>1900</u>, S [?]*, O 27; <u>1901</u>, Ap ?
       Ja 28, Mr 30; <u>1904</u>, Jl 13 (folder FC)

Bryan, William Jennings, cont.

    Jones to Bryan   1900, N 8; 1903, Mr 20

Buck, J. D.   1900, D 27

    Jones to Buck   1901, Mr 25, O 31; 1903, N 30, D 22

Bucke, Richard M.   1899, Jl 21; 1901, F 6, Je 1, Ag 10

    Jones to Bucke   1899, Jl 19; 1901, Ag 6, 14

Burrows, Charles A.   1900, F 10

    Jones to Burrows   1899, Ag 8, S 28, D 4; 1900, Ja 3, 10, F 12,
        S 17; 1901, Mr 12, Ap 18

Burton-Smith, R. H.   1903, My 14, 26, 29

    Jones to Burton-Smith   1903, My 18, 27

Bushnell, Asa S.   1897, N 6; 1899, Ap 3

    Jones to Bushnell   1897, N 3; 1898, Ja 4, My 26, O 19; 1899, Mr 31,
        Je 6, Jl 31, Ag 30

Byers, Joseph P.

    Jones to Byers   1899, F 4, Ap 11; 1902, Ja 29, F 10, 27, S 19

Cady, William E.

    Jones to Cady   1901, Mr 19, Ap 1, 30, My 14, Ag 6; 1902, Ja 8;
        1904, Ja 19

Caldwell, J. W.   1899, Jl 11; 1901, Ap 4; 1904, F 23

    Jones to Caldwell   1899, Ag 5, S 8; 1904, Ja 21, Mr 2

Candee, George   1898, F 15*; 1899, F 9*; 1900, N 1-2* (folder O)

    Jones to Candee   1898, F 11, D 15, 28; 1899, Ap 26, My 10, Ag 15;
        1900, My 16, O 29

Cannon, James A.   1899, Jl 29, 30

    Jones to Cannon   1899, Ag 1*, 8, 11, S 18, O 16; 1900, Ja 3, 9

Carter, Jonathan J.   1897, Je 21, O 18

    Jones to Carter   1897, Je 15, 22, Jl 23, O 16; 1903, O 21

Cassell, (Mrs.) M. E.

    Jones to Cassell   1901, Je 25, S 4; 1902, Ap 8, Je 19, Jl 11

Casson, Herbert N.   1899, F 14, Je 23; 1900, My 19; 1901, Ja 14, Ap 4;
      1902, F 5

   Jones to Casson   1899, Ja 10, F 1, 25, Mr 3, Je 13, 20, 27, Jl 11,
      15, 19, 25, Ag 21, 24; 1900, Jl 18, Ag 30; 1901, Ja 25, Ap 12;
      1902, Ja 30; 1903, N 11; 1904, Ja 5, Ap 7

Churchill, Leroy Sinclair   1899, Mr 16, 20, Ap 4; 1904, Jl [1-12]
      (folder FC)

   Jones to Churchill   1899, Mr 18

Clarke, Charles E.   1900, Ag 4, 23; 1901, F 4, Ag 26 (folder O)

   Jones to Clarke   1900, Ag 7; 1901, F 5

Cleveland Press, Editor

   Jones to Editor, Cleveland Press   1900, Mr 31*; 1903, D 16

Cocolough, William A.   1896, S 26; 1899, Ap 4; 1902, Ja 26; 1904,
      Jl 13 (folder FC)

   Jones to Cocolough   1897, O 18, D 11, 28; 1898, Je 1, S 21, N 18;
      1899, Ja 5, F 17, My 3, Je 19, D 19; 1900, Mr 20, Ag 27; 1901,
      S 10, D 9; 1902, F 22, Ap 22, My 27, Je 10, O 16, D 22; 1903,
      Mr 11, Je 29, Jl 18, 27

Collins, C. P.   1898, Ap 16

   Jones to Collins   1897, Je 12, D 3; 1898, Mr 16; 1901, O 31; 1902,
      F 26, Ag 15, S 8, 15, 17, D 23; 1903, Ja 24, Ap 7; 1904, Mr 3

Colliver, F. B.   1899, Ja 7

   Jones to Colliver   1898, O 19; 1899, Ja 13; 1902, Ja 8, 20

Coming Nation

   Jones to Coming Nation   1898, Ag 26, N 25; 1899, Ap 14; 1900, F 8,
      My 29, Je 11

Chicago Commons (See Taylor, Graham)

Comings, George F.   1899, S 11, D 19; 1901, Ja [?], F 22

   Jones to Comings   1898, O 29; 1900, My 22

Comings, S. H.   1898, My 13, S 15, O 3; 1899, Jl 12

   Jones to Comings   1898, Mr 15, Je 13, Ag 11, 23, S 24, D 16;
      1899, F 2, Jl 13; 1902, F 17, Ap 22, Je 10

The Commonwealth Co.

   Jones to The Commonwealth Co.   1897, N 19; 1898, My 9, Je 30;

47

The Commonwealth Co., cont.

    1901, Ag 14, O 14

Compton, Murat   1898, Ja 19; 1901, Ja 6

    Jones to Compton   1897, O 22*; 1898, F 18, S 23; 1899, Jl 24

Condo, S. S.   1899, My 7, N 17; 1900, S 17, 20

    Jones to Condo   1899, Ap 26, S 11; 1903, Mr 10

Copeland, W. F.

    Jones to Copeland   1900, F 16, My 2, Jl 3, Ag 28; 1901, Ag 9, S 16;
        1903, Je 3, O 22

Cornish, Harris J.   1903, N 7

    Jones to Cornish   1899, My 9; 1901, Je 25, Jl 12, 17, Ag 6, 12,
        S 11, D 9; 1902, F 27; 1903, D 3

Cowell, William   1900, O 4, 21; 1903, Jl 7; 1904, Jl 12 and 13
    (folder FC)

    Jones to Cowell   1899, D 11; 1900, Ja 11, O 5, 22; 1901, O 20;
        1902, S 8; 1903, Mr 12, Jl 8, 15

Cowles, James L.

    Jones to Cowles   1897, Ap 27, Je 23, Jl 6, 7, 19, S 14; 1898, Ja 8,
        13, Ap 26, My 2, Je 15, Jl 20, O 19; 1899, Ja 24, My 27, S 7,
        D 27; 1902, F 27, Ap 5, 25, My 2, 16; 1903, F 6, 12, Jl 2

Crafts, Wilbur F.

    Jones to Crafts   1897, O 28, D 31; 1898, My 10, Je 24

Creager, T. J.   1899, F 19, Mr 25, 26, 27

    Jones to Creager   1899, F 21, Mr 8, 29, Ap 3*

Cromer, P. E.   1902, Mr 20, Ap 18, My 21, N 4; 1903, Ap 8, 18, 27,
    My 15, Je 27

    Jones to Cromer   1902, Ap 14, My 16, 27, Jl 2, 5, N 7; 1903,
        Ap 23, My 11, 18, Je 25

Crosby, Ernest Howard   1897, My 5; 1898, Mr 19, My 6, N 14, D 12, 19;
        1899, Ap 5, 7; 1900, F 28, Ap 3, S 24; 1901, F 9, Je 26; 1902
        Ja 6, Mr 4; 1903, Mr 24, Ap 7; 1904, Ag 28 (folder FC)

    Jones to Crosby   1898, Mr 15, Ap 29, My 25, S 7, N 11, D 7, 15,
        30; 1899, Ap 11; 1900, Ja 23, Mr 1, Ap 6, 30, S 26; 1901, Mr 25,
        Je 24, Jl 20; 1902, F 26, 27, Ap 25, Jl 8, Ag 15, S 26; 1903,
        My 20; 1904, Ja 27

Crunden, Frederick M.   1900, D 28; 1901, Ja 8, F 8, Ap 8; 1902, Ja 10;
                 1903, Mr 24

    Jones to Crunden   1900, O 4; 1901, Ja 30; 1902, Ap 3; 1903, Mr 20

Cullinan, J. S.

    Jones to Cullinan   1901, Ja 21, My 21, N 16, D 26; 1902, Ja 2, 16
                 20, 29, My 21, Je 20; 1903, F 6, D 26; 1904, Mr 22

Dailey, C. W.

    Jones to Dailey   1898, My 27, Ag 6, 22, 23; 1899, Je 17

Darrow, Clarence S.   1900, Ap 14, Je 7, D 28; 1901, Ja 15

    Jones to Darrow   1899, D 23; 1900, Ap 2*, 12, 28, My 29, Je 11, 28,
                 S 22, D 3, 5, 28; 1901, Ja 24, Mr 4, 14, Ap 12, My 1, Jl 18; 1902,
                 Ja 14, F 22, Ap 25, Jl 2, D 11; 1903, F 13, Mr 19, My 19; 1904,
                 F 8, 15

Davidson, R. A.

    Jones to Davidson   1897, Je 22, D 8; 1898, F 25, Ap 18, O 13;
                 1901, Jl 2

Davidson, R. P.   1899, Ap 4; 1902, My 19, 21, 29

    Jones to Davidson   1899, Ag 3; 1902, My 20, 23; 1904, Mr 22

Davidson, Wilbur L.   1899, N 14, D 7; 1902, F 22; 1903, Ap 13, My 1,
                 12, Je 22

    Jones to Davidson   1899, N 18; 1902, F 27; 1903, Ap 29, My 7, Je 25

Davies, David E.   1898, D 22; 1899, My 3, 9; 1901, Ja 16, S 13; 1904,
                 Ap 7

    Jones to Davies   1899, Je 27, Ag 11, 25; 1901, Ja 22, Mr 19, S 21;
                 1902, O 14; 1903, Jl 15, D 1; 1904, Mr 29, Ap 11

Davis, Abner L.   1898, My 5; 1899, S 12; 1901, Mr 6

    Jones to Davis   1898, Ap 22, My 13, 31, Ag 22; 1899, Jl 31, Ag 4,
                 11, D 1; 1900, F 21, Ag 27, S 22

Davis, George T. B.   1898, Mr 7, Je 11, Jl 7, N 4; 1902, Ap 29

    Jones to Davis   1898, Je 13, Jl 7; 1902, My 2

Davis, H. D.

    Jones to Davis   1898, Mr 3, 11, 23, My 2

Dawson, R. P.

    Jones to Dawson   1901, Mr 1, 6; 1902, Ap 3; 1903, Ja 12

Dean, William J.

    Jones to Dean   1897, Je 10, Jl 2; 1898, Mr 1, Jl 1, S 21, N 1, 17;
        1903, Je 16, 19, 22, Jl 2

Debs, Eugene V.   1899, Mr 6, Ap 4, Jl 24, D 8; 1900, N 2* (folder 0);
        1901, D 28; 1904, Jl 13 (folder FC)

    Jones to Debs   1898, D 30; 1899, Je 22, Jl 20, N 29; 1900, S 25

DeWeese, George W.   1903, S 1

    Jones to DeWeese   1899, N 17; 1900, F 3, Mr 22, 26, 28; 1902, D 8,
        11; 1903, My 12, Je 19, 23, 25, S 18

Dillard, James H.   1903, Ja 5, Ap 7, Je 11

    Jones to Dillard   1902, Ja 31, F 22, N 10; 1903, Mr 6, 19, Je 15;
        1904, Ja 28

Dirr, John A. L.

    Jones to Dirr   1898, N 4; 1900, Mr 1, Jl 14; 1901, Mr 20*, Jl 25

Dolan, Thomas J.   1900, F 27, Mr 12, 14, 18

    Jones to Dolan   1900, Mr 1, 13, Ag 27

Donaldson, A. S.

    Jones to Donaldson   1901, Je 7, Ag 8, 28, 0 2, 10

Donaldson, Wilson E.   1898, F 23, Mr 3, 10, 21, 26

    Jones to Donaldson   1898, F 28, Mr 7, 17, 25

Dugan, Jonathan E.   1899, 0 25; 1901, F 11, Mr 25; 1903, Ap 7

    Jones to Dugan   1901, F 14

Dulin, Albert S.

    Jones to Dulin   1899, S 6, 13, 0 3, 10, N 15, D 19; 1900, Ja 13

Dunlap, Samuel P.   1898, Ja 19, F 23, 28, Mr 8, 12, 28; 1899, Ja 10

    Jones to Dunlap   1898, F 7, 21, 22, Mr 8, 15, 18, My 17, 0 29,
        N 4, 23; 1899, Ja 10, Mr 12, Je 1, S 15

Dwyer, Helen Gertrude

    Jones to Dwyer   1900, Jl 5, 9, 16, 20, Ag 4, 24

Dyer, M. A.

    Jones to Dyer   1898, Ap 29, Jl 29; 1899, Mr 9, Ap 15; 1900, F 7;
        1903, My 1

Easley, Ralph M.   1899, My 23, Jl 18, 29

    Jones to Easley   1898, Ja 5; 1899, My 26, Jl 20, S 1; 1901, F 11

Eastern Book Concern (See also Keller & Potts; Keller, A. R.; and Potts,
    J. D.) 1900, Ag 1

Eaton, John   1898, Jl 18, 21, 23 (folder O), Ag 9, 13, 26, S 3, 8;
    1901, Ja 3

    Jones to Eaton   1897, Ag 5; 1898, Jl 16, 20, 22, Ag 8, S 2, 7;
      1899, Ja 11; 1901, O 31, D 19; 1902, Ap 29*, My 1, Je 5, D 16,
      20; 1903, Ja 20, Mr 6, 9, Ap 29, S 15, 29

Eckert, Charles R.   1898, Ag 22

    Jones to Eckert   1898, Ag 23, N 4; 1901, Mr 21, N 20, D 23

Edgerton, J. A.   1900, S 15, 29; 1903, Je 20, Jl 8

    Jones to Edgerton   1900, S 18, 26; 1903, Je 22, Jl 2, 13

Electric Appliance Co.

    Jones to Electric Appliance Co.   1900, D 31; 1901, Ja 5, F 5,
      Mr 7, 22, Ap 11

Ellis, T. H.

    Jones to Ellis   1898, F 7, 9, 26, Mr 2

Evans, J. H.   1892, D 21; 1901, O 21; 1902, Ja 6

    Jones to Evans   1901, Ja 21, O 28; 1903, Jl 24; 1904, Ja 13, Ap 28

Farnsworth, A. M.

    Jones to Farnsworth   1899, F 16, S 8; 1900, N 16, 19, 27; 1903,
      Ap 29

Ferguson, Charles   1901, Ja 30, F 6; 1903, Mr 23*, Ap 7, 13, 15*, 18,
    24, 25, 29, My 1, 3, Jl 7

    Jones to Ferguson   1901, Ja 26; 1902, Ja 30, N 4, D 2, 8, 19; 1903,
    Ja 29, F 25, Mr 19, Ap 7, 23, 28, My 1

Ferguson, Georgia Ransom (Mrs. Charles)   1903, Ap 7, 14, Jl 22, O 19,
    N 7; 1904, Mr 6, 7

    Jones to Ferguson   1903, Ap 10, N 5; 1904, Mr 8

Ferriss, James H.   1899, Ap 4, N 8; 1902, D 22

    Jones to Ferriss   1898, N 28, D 16; 1899, Ap 15, Je 22; 1901, F 5;
            1902, D 27

Fillebrown, C. B.   1898, Je 24, Jl 5; 1899, Ap 12, 21, Je 27

    Jones to Fillebrown   1898, Je 28, Jl 7, 14, 16, S 2, 14; 1899,
            F 2, Je 23

Finch, S. M.   1898, Ap 26, Jl 15; 1899, Ap 4

    Jones to Finch   1897, Jl 15; 1898, Ap 28, Jl 20; 1899, Mr 18

Fisk, D. M.   1898, Ja 6, 10; 1900, Jl 14; 1901, D 27; 1904, Jl 13
            (folder FC)

    Jones to Fisk   1897, Je 2, D 23; 1898, Ja 8, 12, D 31; 1899, Ja 12;
            1900, Je 9, Jl 18; 1901, D 30; 1903, Ja 28

Fleming, William   1901, Ja 2

    Jones to Fleming   1897, Je 17; 1900, S 8, O 3

Fletcher, Horace   1898, O 18

    Jones to Fletcher   1898, O 21*; 1899, F 7

Flower, B. O.   1899, Ja 3, 19, Ap 6; 1901, Ja 24; 1903, Ja 20, Mr 25,
            Ap 9, O 19

    Jones to Flower   1899, Ja 11, F 13, Ap 8, 14, S 8; 1900, My 12;
            1901, F 15; 1902, Mr 31, Ap 8, Je 4; 1903, Ja 22, O 20; 1904,
            Ja 8

Flowers, J. W.   1904, Jl 15 (folder FC)

    Jones to Flowers   1900, F 21; 1901, S 21; 1902, N 21, 29; 1903,
            F 25

Flynn, W. Earl

    Jones to Flynn   1901, D 31; 1902, F 19, My 27, Je 10, 19, Jl 2,
            S 11, O 24, 30

Foote, Allen R.

    Jones to Foote   1898, N 2; 1899, Ja 30, F 28, Mr 28, Ag 5

Frost, William G.

    Jones to Frost   1897, N 23, D 13; 1898, Ja 5, Jl 8; 1899, Ja 19,
            Ap 3; 1901, My 21

Funk and Wagnalls Co.   1899, Ap 4

Funk and Wagnalls Co., cont.

    Jones to Funk and Wagnalls   1901, Ja 30, F 8, Je 3, 14, D 23;
        1902, Ja 30

Funk, I. K. (See Funk and Wagnalls Co.)

Gates, George A.   1897, My 5; 1899, Ap 5, 20, My 17, Je 19, S 19

    Jones to Gates   1897, My 10; 1899, Ap 17, 26, My 25, Je 22, O 4

Gavit, John P.   1898, O 28; 1899, Ja 2-4, Ap 4, My 1, S 24, N 10;
        1902, F 9, 19, My 21, N 24; 1903, Ap 7, Je 9, Jl 5; 1904, Jl 13
        (folder FC)

    Jones to Gavit   1897, Je 2, Ag 12, N 18, 23; 1898, Je 24, N 2,
        D 31; 1899, F 21, My 3; 1901, Mr 28; 1902, Ja 28, Ap 25, My 22,
        28, Je 10, D 22; 1903, My 20, Je 29; 1904, My 11

Gear, W. C.   1900, S 26, 29, O 1*, 3, 6

    Jones to Gear   1900, S 27, O 2

Ghent, W. J.   1899, Ap 7, Je 12, N 5; 1900, Jl 16; 1901, Ap [?];
        1903, Mr 24

    Jones to Ghent   1899, Ap 14, Je 1, D 1, 8; 1900, Mr 28, Jl 18,
        Ag 2; 1901, Mr 28, S 11; 1902, S 22

Gibson, George Howard   1899, Ja 4, Ap 8; 1901, Ja 4, 21

    Jones to Gibson   1898, O 14, D 23; 1899, Ja 6, Je 1, Ag 26; 1900,
        F 16, 21; 1901, Ja 5, 22; 1904, Mr 25

Gibson, W. E.

    Jones to Gibson   1901, N 7; 1902, Ap 14, Je 21, Ag 15

Gignoux, R. M.   1899, Ap 5

    Jones to Gignoux   1898, F 18, Ag 26; 1899, Ja 10

Gilkison, B. F.   1899, Ap 13

    Jones to Gilkison   1897, N 8; 1898, F 25, 28, Jl 5, 14, 20, Ag 23,
        S 14, O 14; 1899, F 4, 21, Ap 15, My 11, 18, Jl 13, 18; 1901
        Ap 15, My 13

Gilman, (Mrs.) Charlotte (Perkins) Stetson   1899, S 22; 1901, O 2

    Jones to Gilman   1898, D 31; 1899, Ja 3, Mr 17, O 5

Gladden, Washington   1897, D 7, 14; 1899, Mr 4, Ap 3, 13; 1900, F 20

    Jones to Gladden   1897, Ap 21, 28, D 8, 16; 1898, Mr 10, 22, S 22,
        28, N 8, D 28; 1899, Ap 15, My 12, S 26; 1900, F 13, 19, Ap 5;

Gladden, Washington, cont.

    1901, O 3; 1903, Ap 23

Gleason, H. W.

   Jones to Gleason   1898, F 7, Je 4, Jl 19, Ag 10; 1899, Ap 17

Goldman, Meta E. (Mrs. Eugene)   1903, S 17, 23, O 2, D 14; 1904,
    Ja 26, 31, F 4, 19

   Jones to Goldman   1903, S 18, 24, D 16; 1904, Ja 28, F 5

Gompers, Samuel   1899, Ap 5; 1900, Ja 26; 1902, Je 27, Ag 1, N 28;
    1903, F 27, Jl 14; 1904, Jl 8

   Jones to Gompers   1897, O 29; 1898, Ap 28; 1899, S 25; 1902,
    Je 30*; 1903, Mr 23, Jl 17; 1904, Jl 13

Goodyear, (Mrs.) Anna Forbes

   Jones to Goodyear   1897, Ap 26; 1899, Ja 13, My 29; 1900, Je 25;
    1901, Jl 2

Gordon, W. H. (Mr. & Mrs.)

   Jones to Gordon   1897, S 9, 14*, O 26; 1898, D 16; 1902, Ja 2

Grant, Frederick   1898, O 27; 1900, Ap 24

   Jones to Grant   1898, N 7; 1900, S 17

Green, J. T. R.

   Jones to Green   1898, Ja 12, Jl 20, O 21; 1899, D 27; 1900, My 17

Grimes, G. W.

   Jones to Grimes   1897, My 24, Jl 19, 21; 1898, Je 3

Gunckel, J. E.   1898, Mr 30; 1902, O 13

   Jones to Gunckel   1898, Ap 1; 1902, O 13

Hall, Bolton   1898, Je 16, Jl 13*, D 15; 1899, O 12; 1901, Ap 6; 1902,
    Mr 31

   Jones to Hall   1898, Je 13, 21, Jl 21, S 7, N 2, D 7, 28; 1901,
    Ap 12; 1903, D 24

Hamilton, Frank   1900, S 15

   Jones to Hamilton   1899, Je 24; 1900, Jl 24, S 18

Hammond, Ernest W.   1899, Ap 4

Hammond, Ernest W., cont.

Jones to Hammond   1897, O 20, N 3, D 28; 1898, Ja 4, F 7, 14, 16,
    26, Mr 10, 18, 29, Ap 30, Je 3, 14, 21, 28, Jl 15, 20, Ag 10,
    24, S 6, O 12, 31, D 6, 16, 28; 1899, F 17, Mr 14, My 17, Jl 11,
    Ag 25, S 15, N 22, D 9; 1900, Ja 12, Mr 5, Ap 9, 16, My 3, 12,
    28, Je 27, Jl 3, 13, 20, Ag 8*, S 10, N 8; 1901, Ja 4, 24, 26,
    30, 31, Mr 4, 6, 11, 15, 27, 30, Ap 1, 4, 10, My 5, 6, 11, 28;
    1902, Ag 15; 1903, F 25

Hammond, Nellie L. (Mrs. Ernest W.)

Jones to Hammond   1897, D 13; 1898, D 7; 1899, Ja 5; 1901, My 16,
    Je 12, Ag 6; 1902, Mr 31

Hampton, George P.   1899, Ag 1, 6

Jones to Hampton   1899, S 13; 1900, Jl 12; 1901, Je 26; 1902, My 15

Hardee, William

Jones to Hardee   1899, Ap 14; 1901, Ap 30, N 5, 11

Hardison, James H.   1899, Ap 4; 1904, Jl 14 (folder FC)

Jones to Hardison   1898, Mr 2, My 31, Je 10, Ag 5, S 22, 28, N 2,
    D 16, 28; 1901, Ja 22, Ap 17, S 18; 1903, Ja 8

Hare, Charles

Jones to Hare   1897, S 1; 1898, D 6; 1899, Jl 19, D 7; 1903, F 25

Harris, Lem. P.

Jones to Harris   1897, S 24; 1900, Jl 31; 1902, My 28, N 7; 1903,
    Mr 9

Haskell, Charles C.

Jones to Haskell   1902, Ap 4, My 8, Je 9; 1903, Ja 22

Hayes, Max S.   1899, S 11, 13, 17, O 9

Jones to Hayes   1899, S 12, 15

Hazel, Oscar J.   1901, O 13

Jones to Hazel   1899, Je 7, 13, 17, O 30; 1901, O 14, 28; 1903,
    My 8

Hearst, William Randolph   1900, My 15, S 21*

Jones to Hearst   1900, S 21, 26; 1902, D 15; 1903, Mr 20

Heermans, W. S. H.   [Hennans, W. S. H.; Hermans, W. S. H.?]

   Jones to Heermans [Hennans; Hermans?]   1898, Je 14, 22, S 22;
       1901, N 8; 1902, O 14, N 21; 1903, O 13; 1904, Mr 15, 29

Hennans, W. S. H.   (See W. S. H. Heermans)

Hermans, W. S. H.   (See W. S. H. Heermans)

Herring, Hubert C.   1898, Mr 7; 1904, Ap 5, 10, My 24

   Jones to Herring   1898, Mr 17; 1904, Ap 7, 11

Herron, George D.   1898, Ap 28, S 15, 24, O 28, D 31; 1901, My 10

   Jones to Herron   1897, O 25; 1898, Ja 13, 22, F 11, 25, Mr 10,
       Ap 23, S 16, 20, N 2, D 29, 31; 1899, Ja 4, F 17, 25, Mr 2,
       9, Jl 12, 22, S 7, O 12, N 16; 1900, S 26, O 12, 20, N 21,
       D 4; 1901, My 1, 21; 1904, Ap 13

Hickman, George M.   1897, N 16, D 21; 1898, N 14; 1899, Ja 2; 1902,
       Ja 14

   Jones to Hickman   1897, D 23; 1899, Ja 5

Holmes, Frank W.

   Jones to Holmes   1897, Jl 6, 15, Ag 26, S 23, O 8; 1901, Ja 28

Holt, Hamilton   1898, O 10, 17, N 17, D 30; 1899, Ja 25, My 29; 1901,
       Ag 26; 1903, Ap 10, Je 20, Jl 7

   Jones to Holt   1898, O 13, N 12, 17; 1899, F 2, 7; 1901, Ag 29;
       1903, Je 25

Hooker, George E.   1898, F 14, My 20, Je 3, 29; 1899, Ap 26; 1901,
       Ja 3; 1904, Jl 13 (folder FC)

   Jones to Hooker   1897, Ag 24, N 1, 16, 18, D 3, 8, 29; 1898, Ja 13,
       F 9, 25, My 12, 25, Je 6, S 24; 1899, Jl 19; 1900, Je 7, 25,
       Ag 25; 1901, Ap 12; 1903, Jl 3

Hopkins, H. J.

   Jones to Hopkins   1898, Ag 22, O 19, D 16, 29; 1901, My 27; 1903,
       F 6

Houston, James   1900, Mr 22, 26

   Jones to Houston   1900, Mr 23*, My 10, 29, Je 2

Howe, M. S.

   Jones to Howe   1897, D 21; 1898, Ap 12; 1899, My 4; 1900, S 13;
       1901, S 17

Howells, W. D.   1898, D 18; 1903, Ap 7

Jones to Howells   1898, D 21

Howland, William B.   1899, Mr 10, Ap 4, 10, 14

Jones to Howland   1899, Mr 14, Ap 8, 17, My 4, 16, Je 1, 13;
    1903, Ja 17

Hubbard, Elbert   1899, Ag 25; 1901, Ap 4; 1902, S 12; 1903, Ap 27;
    1904, Ja 28, Jl 13 (folder FC)

Jones to Hubbard   1899, Ag 26; 1900, Ja 10, Ap 7; 1902, Je 23,
    Jl 14; 1903, F 19, Ap 29; 1904, Ja 20, Ap 13

Hughes, V. R.

Jones to Hughes   1901, Ja 31, Mr 1, 6, 12, 16, 18, 26, Ap 1*, 8,
    11, 17, 23, My 5, 7, 13, 14, 20, 23, 28, Je 3*, Jl 9

Hyde, Albert Marion   1904, Jl 12 (folder FC)

Jones to Hyde   1897, D 21; 1898, N 25; 1901, N 5

The International Society

Jones to The International Society   1897, S 17; 1898, Je 10, Ag 9,
    S 6

Jenkins, O.   1898, S 20; 1899, N 8

Jones to Jenkins   1898, S 21; 1899, S 11; 1900, O 19; 1901, S 11

Jermain, Sylvanus P.   1897, S 16; 1899, S 10

Jones to Jermain   1897, Ja 14; 1898, O 28, N 23; 1902, Ap 5

Johnson, Henry V.   1901, Ja 5

Jones to Johnson   1898, S 6; 1899, S 13; 1901, Ja 24; 1904, My 25

Johnson, Lyman H.   1899, F 17, O 18; 1902, My 5; 1903, Ja 2

Jones to Johnson   1899, F 20; 1902, Ap 29; 1903, Ja 5

Johnson, Tom L.   1901, Jl 23, O 26; 1902, My 3, S 27; 1903, Mr 23,
    Ap 8, O 28; 1904, My 18, Jl 2

Jones to Johnson   1900, N 13, 21, D 1; 1901, F 5, 8, 19, Ap 12,
    My 17, Jl 3, Ag 15, N 27; 1902, My 2, S 8, 22, 26, O 4; 1903,
    F 2, Mr 21, Jl 16, Ag 10, S 1, O 29, N 2

Johnson, Willis

Jones to Johnson   1899, S 8, 18, 27; 1900, O 29

Jonathan, Edward and Mary Ellen   1904, Jl 13 (folder FC)

    Jones to Jonathan   1897, My 14; 1898, My 3; 1902, My 19, N 24;
        1903, F 25

Jones, Daniel E.   1904, Jl 12 and 13* (folder FC)

    Jones to Jones, Daniel E.   1897, Ag 17, 21, O 12; 1902, Je 9;
        1904, Ap 13

Jones, Ellen M. "Nell"   1904, Jl 13 (folder FC)

    Jones to Jones, Ellen M.   1898, Jl 29; 1899, Ja 6, Ag 3, D 1

Jones, Helen Beach (Mrs. Samuel M.)   Correspondence 1898-1912,
    66 letters (folder FC); 1901, Ja 10

Jones, James K.   1900, S 22, O 8, 20

    Jones to Jones, James K.   1900, S 24, O 9, 22

Jones, Jenkin Lloyd (Mr. & Mrs.)   1899, Ag 26, Ag [?], O 20, N 22; 1904,
    F 3, 10, 18, Mr 4

    Jones to Jones, Jenkin Lloyd   1899, F 27, Jl 25, Ag 30, N 15, D 1,
        19; 1901, F 5, O 31; 1902, S 23; 1903, Ja 6; 1904, F 8, 12, 20,
        24, Mr 2

Jones, John H.

    Jones to Jones, John H.   1897, Je 7, Jl 24, O 18, D 17; 1898, S 16;
        1899, Jl 24; 1900, O 22

Jones, Lloyd   1898, Je 27, Jl 8; 1899, Jl 17

    Jones to Jones, Lloyd   1898, Jl 1, Ag 12, 22; 1900, Ap 20; 1901,
        My 6

Jones, Paul Hugh   1896, N 22 (folder FC); 1904, Jl 13* and 14 (folder FC)

    Jones to Jones, Paul Hugh   1898, Ag 8, 12; 1900, My 4, 14, 24, 28,
        Je 11, Jl 28; 1901, Mr 2; 1903, F 12, 25, Mr 4, 11; 1904, Mr 26,
        Ap 6, 13, My 6

Jones, Percy Curtiss   1904, Jl 13* and 14 (folder FC)

    Jones to Jones, Percy Curtiss   1897, O 8, 11, D 1; 1898, F 21,
        Mr 1, 8, 10*, 18, 22, Ap 1, My 3, 7, 16, 21, 23, 31, Je 6, 10,
        13, 18, 21, 29, Jl 7, 12; 1900, Ap 9, Je 18, Ag 13, S 8, D 3,
        5; 1901, Ja 3, 23, 24, F 6*, 13, 20, Mr 6, 9, 12, 13, 25, 27,
        Ap 5, 18, 22, 26, 30, My 9, 28, Je 7, 12, 18, 22, 25, Jl 2,
        9, 22, 30, Ag 16, 31, S 3, O 28, 30, N 16, 21, D 4, 14; 1902,
        Ja 24, 28, 29, F 7, 12, 14, 17, Ap 8, 22, My 5; 1903, F 19

Jones, Roy R.

    Jones to Jones, Roy R.   1902, F 22; 1903, My 13, 26, S 2, D 2, 21;

Jones, Roy R., cont.

       1904, Ja 6, F 24, My 11

Jones, S. C. D. (See Jones, Mrs. Jenkin Lloyd)

Jones, Mrs. Samuel Milton (See Jones, Helen Beach)

Jones, T. D.

   Jones to Jones, T. D.   1898, D 6, 9; 1899, Ja 5, S 11

Joslyn, Charles A.   1900, F 9

   Jones to Joslyn   1900, Ja 18, F 12, N 28; 1903, O 5

Keller & Potts (See also Eastern Book Concern; Keller, A. R.; and
        Potts, J. D.)

   Jones to Keller & Potts   1899, Je 20, Jl 1, 4, 6, 7, 11, 12, 13,
      18, 20, 22, 24, 25, S 6, D 6, 11

Keller, A. R. (See also Eastern Book Concern; Keller & Potts; and
        Potts, J. D.)   1899, Ap 19, My 11

Kellogg, J. H.   1898, Ag 10

   Jones to Kellogg   1898, F 1, 3, Mr 11, Ag 5, 24, N 12

Kellogg, Will K.   1898, F 11

   Jones to Kellogg   1897, O 29

Kerr, Charles H.   1900, Mr 1

   Jones to Kerr   1897, D 10; 1898, Ja 8, My 13, O 12; 1899, F 3;
      1900, F 27, Mr 27, My 10, Jl 26, O 12, 19; 1901, D 6, 20; 1903,
      F 13, 25; 1904, Ap 28

Kerr, John B.

   Jones to Kerr   1897, Jl 10, 19, Ag 23; 1902, Ap 14, 21

Keyes, Edward T.   1898, S 29, O 1, 5; 1899, Ap 4, Je 9, N 8; 1900, D 26;
      1902, Ja 11; 1903, D 4

   Jones to Keyes   1898, S 8, 14, O 3, 18, N 8, 16; 1899, Mr 9,
      Je 13, Jl 6, S 18, D 9; 1900, Mr 26, Jl 16, 21, 24, Ag 8, 13;
      1901, Je 12; 1902, Ja 14, Je 4, 23, D 27; 1903, Mr 7; 1904,
      My 16

Keyes, Franklin C.

   Jones to Keyes   1902, Ja 8, 29, F 7, 22, 26

Kilbourne, James   1901, Ap 2, 13; 1904, Jl 15 (folder FC)

Kilbourne, James, cont.

    Jones to Kilbourne   1899, My 24; 1900, Je 28; 1901, F 1, Je 22,
        O 9; 1903, F 20, 26

Klein, Nicholas   1900, S 15

    Jones to Klein   1900, My 1, Ag 6, S 18

Kling, W. A.   1898, Ja 18, F 14, 15

    Jones to Kling   1897, My 24, Je 8; 1898, Ja 20, F 15, O 31, N 18;
        1899, F 6; 1900, F 8

Klinke, Henry C.

    Jones to Klinke   1899, My 5; 1901, Ap 1; 1902, Ap 14, D 11; 1903,
    My 19

Kuehn, Herman

    Jones to Kuehn   1901, Jl 20, D 9; 1902, My 8, 15, Je 23, 26;
        1903, My 23; 1904, My 10

Lamson, W. F.   1899, Ag 26, 31, N 9; 1900, Mr 9

    Jones to Lamson   1899, Ag 21, S 1

Law, Mary E.   1900, D 25; 1901, Ap 30; 1902, D 30

    Jones to Law   1898, N 7, D 24; 1901, Ap 30, N 6

Lentz, John J.   1899, F 15, Ap 3; 1900, Ag 17, 31; 1901, Ap 2; 1903,
    Ap 8, My 18*, Je 1, 5

    Jones to Lentz   1899, F 21; 1900, Ag 27; 1901, F 8; 1902, My 8;
        1903, Ap 10, My 19, Je 3, 15, Jl 29

Leonard, J. R.   1904, Jl 13 (folder FC)

    Jones to Leonard   1897, O 15, N 8, 24, D 3, 16; 1898, Ja 17, 26,
        Mr 9, Ap 23, 28; 1899, My 11; 1901, Ag 8, O 31, D 23; 1903, Ja 22

Lewis, Owen J.   1898, S 19; 1901, Ja 14

    Jones to Lewis   1898, S 20; 1901, Ja 22

Ley, John   1899, Ap 4; 1900, D 26; 1902, Ja 6; 1903, Je 22

    Jones to Ley   1897, Ap 24, D 8; 1898, Mr 30, Ap 15, Ag 26, O 13,
        D 29; 1899, Ap 15; 1901, Mr 12, D 17; 1903, Ap 7, Je 23

Lloyd, Henry Demarest   1897, Mr 23, My 5; 1898, O 22 (folder O), N 10,
        22, D 13 (folder O); 1899, Ap 24, Ag 7, 28, N 29, D 30; 1900,
        Ja 5, Ap 7; 1901, D 31

Lloyd, Henry Demarest, cont.

    Jones to Lloyd   1896, D 14, 26; 1897, Ja 10, 19, F 1, 6, 15, Mr 20,
        22, 25, Ap 6, 16, 28, My 11, 28, Je 15, N 23*, D 6, 10, 14; 1898,
        F 9, 11, 25, Mr 3, 19, Je 27, Jl 12, Ag 18, S 7, 22, O 20, 25, 28,
        N 5, 18; 1899, Ja 2, Jl 29, Ag 24, S 2, D 2; 1900, Ja 2, Ap 3; 1902,
        Ja 18

Lockwood, M. L.   1899, S 20

    Jones to Lockwood   1899, O 5, 11, 16; 1901, My 28

Low, A. H.

    Jones to Low   1897, S 14*; 1898, O 20; 1900, F 6, 20, My 19; 1901,
        Mr 16, Ap 1; 1903, O 30

MacBroom, J. C. (Mr. & Mrs.)

    Jones to MacBroom   1898, Mr 10, Jl 14; 1900, My 1; 1901, S 27, D 18

McCullagh, W. J.   1901, D 8

    Jones to McCullagh   1897, O 8; 1898, D 6; 1901, Ap 24, 26, D 12

McDonald, F. A.

    Jones to McDonald   1901, Ap 8, My 24, Je 8, 12

McDowell, Mary E.   1899, Je 10, N 5; 1900, Mr 30

    Jones to McDowell   1900, Ap 3; 1901, My 5

MacFadden, Barnarr   1903, Je 29, Jl 30

    Jones to MacFadden   1901, D 30; 1902, O 14, 28, N 4, D 10; 1903,
        Ja 30, My 20, Jl 2, O 21, N 6, D 22

McFadden, C. K.

    Jones to McFadden   1902, D 20; 1903, Ja 8, 27, F 16, My 11

McGee, I. J.   1903, My 11, Je 11, 16

    Jones to McGee   1903, My 12, Je 15, 17

McGuire, James K.   1900, Ja 2, D 27; 1903, Ja 2

    Jones to McGuire   1899, Mr 9; 1901, D 20; 1902, Ja 2

McKinley, William   1898, Jl 18

    Jones to McKinley   1897, Ap 24, Jl 21, O 15, N 17; 1898, Jl 15

McMahon, M. H.   1903, My 15; 1904, F 2, 20

McMahon, M. H., cont.

    Jones to McMahon   1898, S 6, N 4; 1903, My 20; 1904, F 8

McNamee, John F.   1898, N 16; 1899, Ap 5

    Jones to McNamee   1898, N 17; 1899, Ap 15, Je 13, 26, Jl 1, 12

Mann, Horace   1903, Ap 8, My 18, Jl 7

    Jones to Mann   1899, Ap 3; 1900, Je 7; 1903, Ap 10, My 20, Ag 10

Markham, Edwin   1899, Je 18, 19, 27, Jl 20, Ag 14; 1900, F 18, S 1, D 29;
        1901, Ja 17, My 9; 1903, Ja 8

    Jones to Markham   1899, My 19, Je 5, Jl 5, 24, Ag 19; 1900, S 6;
        1901, My 14

Matteson, Claude

    Jones to Matteson   1897, N 22; 1898, Mr 3, My 3, 16; 1901, My 3, 9,
        21, Je 10, Jl 22

Matteson, David E. (Dr. & Mrs.)   1899, Ap 4; 1904, Je 1

    Jones to Matteson   1899, Ja 11; 1900, My 25; 1903, Je 10

Matteson, Ted A.

    Jones to Matteson   1897, Je 21, Jl 2, Ag 5, S 10, 23, O 4, N 3,
        19, D 28; 1898, F 23; 1901, Ja 23; 1902, F 22, S 19

Maxwell, Frank (Mr. & Mrs.)   1904, Jl 12 (folder FC)

    Jones to Maxwell   1898, Jl 2, 15, Ag 9, 31, S 12, O 19; 1899, Je 16,
        Ag 8, O 3; 1900, Je 19; 1901, Ja 22, 24, F 9*, 26 Mr 9, Ap 5, 17,
        24, My 16, 22, Je 20, 25, Jl 2, 12, 18, Ag 7, 17, S 6, 13, 21, O 2,
        N 5, 9, 16, 22, D 4, 12, 26, 31; 1902, Ja 2, 18, 24, 30, F 7, 19,
        Ap 4, 23, 25, My 17, Je 10, Jl 2, 5, S 22, 26, O 6, 17, N 7, 20,
        25, D 16, 30; 1903, Ja 3, 19, 28, F 5, 20, Mr 25, Ap 23, My 6, 13,
        25, Je 5, Jl 2, 14, 18, 23, 29, Ag 15, S 9, 22, 26, O 15, 26, N 2,
        30, D 8, 12, 17, 21, 28; 1904, Ja 6, 13, 19, F 9, 15, Mr 1, 3, 16,
        23, Ap 13, My 11, 19, Je 15

Mead, Edwin D. (Mr. & Mrs.)   1899, Ap 4, 24, Je 27 (folder O); 1902,
        S 29

    Jones to Mead   1898, F 28; 1900, My 5, O 8; 1902, S 19, O 30; 1904,
        Ja 12

Meagher, M. W.   1900, My 30, Je 8

    Jones to Meagher   1900, Ap 4, Je 2, 11

Meily, George H.   1899, Ap 4, O 9; 1900, S 21

Meily, George H., cont.

    Jones to Meily   1899, O 11; 1900, S 26

Merrell, John B.   1897, Ap 21; 1902, Mr 13; 1903, Mr [?]

    Jones to Merrell   1897, My 13, Ag 16; 1898, F 14, My 27; 1899, F 3;
        1900, Mr 7, Ap 5, N 30; 1901, Ap 4; 1903, Ap 24; 1904, Mr 2

Meserole, Darwin J.   1899, Ap 4, O 29, N 5; 1901, Ja 1

    Jones to Meserole   1899, My 29; 1900, Ja 11, N 17, 30; 1901, Ja 22,
        F 4, 5, Mr 25, Ap 4, 23, My 16, 20, Je 17, Jl 12, O 28

Meserole, Katherine L. Maltby (Mrs. Darwin J.)   1899, Ap 4; 1900, Ja 9,
        Ap 11; 1901, Ja 1

    Jones to Meserole   1897, S 14; 1900, Ja 11; 1903, O 30

Mettler, Peter J.   1903, Mr 2

    Jones to Mettler   1897, D 29; 1899, Ja 5, Mr 10, O 9; 1901, F 5

Millard, Irwin I.   1898, My 17, Ag 23; 1900, D 25

    Jones to Millard   1897, My 26; 1898, Ja 12, Ag 26, S 15

Mills, Benjamin Fay   1898, Ja 5, My 6, O 22, 27, D 2, 31; 1899, Ja 3,
        7, 21, Ap 4, 24, My 11

    Jones to Mills   1897, Ap 21, My 1, 14, Je 21, Jl 17, Ag 7*, 28,
        N 23; 1898, Ja 17, F 10, Mr 25, Ap 26, My 3, 17, Ag 31, O 19,
        31, D 5, 20, 30; 1899, Ja 3, 5, F 2, Mr 7, My 10, 27, Je 22,
        Jl 14, S 12, 27, N 28; 1903, Ap 24, S 18; 1904, My 11

Monnett, Frank S.   1901, Ja 5, Ap 2

    Jones to Monnett   1898, Mr 1; 1899, Je 20, 23; 1900, S 26

Montgomery, Samuel   1898, S 4; 1902, Ag 18

    Jones to Montgomery   1898, Mr 22; 1899, F 15; 1900, S 25; 1902,
        S 2; 1903, Mr 17; 1904, F 20

Morgan, M. H.   1901, Ja 2

    Jones to Morgan   1897, Je 11, N 8; 1898, O 12; 1899, Mr 10, Ap 12,
        Je 27, Ag 18, O 11; 1903, Ap 19

Morrison, Frank   1903, O 17

    Jones to Morrison   1900, Jl 20; 1903, O 13, 19

Morrison, J. A.

    Jones to Morrison   1898, Ap 22; 1899, Mr 14; 1900, Jl 25; 1901, Je 8

Morse, E. L.   1899, Mr 7; 1903, Ja 2, O 2

   Jones to Morse   1900, Ag 9; 1903, O 28

Motsinger, N. H.

   Jones to Motsinger   1899, My 8, Je 5, 16, Ag 26, S 1; 1900, F 10,
      Mr 22

Mulholland, John   1900, D 1, 26; 1903, D 8, 10

   Jones to Mulholland   1900, D 4; 1903, D 8

Munsey, Frank A.   1901, Ag 6, D 30

   Jones to Munsey   1901, F 6, Jl 30, Ag 7, S 11, D 23

Munsey's Magazine   (See Munsey, Frank A.)

Munson, Mary F.   1897, N 20

   Jones to Munson   1897, D 29; 1899, F 28; 1900, N 8

Nelson, Nelson Olsen   1898, F 21, Mr 5, 24, Ap 1, 6, 9, 25, My 11, 28,
      Je 1, 2, 11, 18, Jl 10*, 11, 18, 21*, 31, Ag 15, 24, 29, S 12,
      17, O 17, N 3, 11, 22, D 2, 14, 16, 23; 1899, Ja 6, 11, 17, 18,
      27, 29, F 5, 13, 14, 17, 23, 27, Mr 3*, 17, Ap 4*, 8, 26, My 9,
      11, 26, Je 21, Jl 11*, 13, 14*, 21, 25, 29, Ag 1, 11, 14, 29, S 6,
      10, 13, 14, 18, 25, 27, 28, O 11, 28, N 15, 22, 23, D 13, D [?];
      1900, Ja 23, F 12, Mr 9, 30, Ap 4, 18, My 11, 20, Je 19, 21, Jl 9,
      15, 24, 25, 26, Ag 7, 14, 22 (folder O), Ag [?], S 3 (folder O),
      18, 22, 24, 25, O 8, 11, 15, 22, 26, 31, N 2, 6, 7, 10, D 22*, 24;
      1900 [?]; 1901, Ja 2, Ja [?], F 4, Mr 2, Ap 1, 2, 8, 13, 23, My 3,
      22, 27, Je 2, Jl 20, Ag 26 (folder O), S 10, 17, 28, O 11, 17,
      N 5, 11, 26, 27, D 20, 24, 27*, 28; 1902, Ja 13, 20, 27, Ja [?],
      F 4, 25, F [?], Ap 1, 10, My 15, 16, Je 14, 21, 30, Jl 3, 5, 6,
      Ag 16, S 11, O 8*, 9, N 20, D 8, 15; 1903, Ja 12, 14, F 13, Mr 11,
      Ap 1, 7, 9, 12, 27, My 4, 7, 27*, 30, Je 18, Jl 15, Ag 8, 12, 22,
      S 4, O 12, 30, N 9, 16, 25, O - N [?], N [?], D 14 (folder O), 24;
      1904, Ja 4, 12, 26, 27, Ja [?], F 2, 6, 13, 20, 25, 26, F [?],
      Mr 1, 3, 4, 12, 28, Ap 1, 9, Ja - Ap [?], Jl 7, 12 (folder FC),
      [ND*], [ND] (folder O)

   Jones to Nelson   1898, Mr 9, 22, Ap 19, My 2, 24, Je 1, 20, Jl 6,
      13, 20, 29, Ag 26, S 7, O 15, N 10, 14, 21, 29, D 9, 15, 21;
      1899, Ja 11, F 2, 10, 15, Mr 2, Ap 17, 28, My 9, 10, 13, Je 3,
      20, 23, Jl 12, 14, 21, 31, Ag 11, 19, 26, 30, S 7, 8, 15, 23, 27,
      O 2, 10, 17, N 13, 17; 1900, F 6, Mr 1, 12, Ap 5, 16, 28, My 12,
      29, Je 16, 18, Jl 14, 19, 25, 28, Ag 6, 14, S 6, 20, 25, O 5, 9,
      12, 19, 23, N 5, 8, 12, 16, D 20, 28; 1901, Ja 23, 25, F 6, Mr 5,
      Ap 12, My 1, 22, 28, Jl 2, 19, Ag 12, 15, S 6, 13, 25, O 30, N 11,
      20, 29, D 23, 26, 30; 1902, Ja 11, 23, 28, F 8, 19, Ap 7, 25,
      Je 11, 17, Jl 2, 5, Ag 15, S 13, O 13, D 2, 22; 1903, Ja 6, F 6,
      Mr 6, 18, Ap 29, My 8, 18, 27, Je 25, Jl 17, 29, Ag 4, 10, S 9,
      O 17, 23, N 3, 6, D 1, 22; 1904, Ja 20, F 2, 13, 17, 24, 29,
      Mr 10, 16, 25, Ap 6, 13, My 19, 25, Je 23

New York Journal   1901, Ap 2

    Jones to New York Journal   1899, My 4; 1900, My 15; 1901, S 4, D 6;
        1903, D 16

Newcomb, C. B.   1900, Ag 7, N 19, D 27; 1901, D 28

    Jones to Newcomb   1900, Jl 20, N 22; 1902, Jl 2, O 16

Newton, R. Herber   1899, F 7, Ap 11; 1900, F 10

    Jones to Newton   1899, F 21, Ap 25

Nicewanger, W: H.

    Jones to Nicewanger   1898, Je 16; 1901, Je 3, 25, Jl 11, 15, 18

Noe, A. Allen

    Jones to Noe   1899, Je 20, 24, S 8, 12, D 15

O'Brien, Patrick   1898, F 25, Mr 3; 1899, Ap 4; 1900, D 11; 1901, Ja 10;
    1902, My 9; 1903, Ap 8, My 9; 1904, Jl 8

    Jones to O'Brien   1898, Mr 2, O 29; 1899, Ja 10, F 23, Je 29; 1900,
        Mr 5, My 7, S 14, N 13; 1901, Ja 29, Ap 12; 1902, D 10

O'Day, Daniel   1899, Ap 4; 1901, Ja 10; 1902, Ja 10; 1903, Ap 7

    Jones to O'Day   1898, N 26; 1899, Ja 11; 1903, Ap 7

Olmstead, C. George

    Jones to Olmstead   1901, N 14; 1903, Mr 4, 18, 20

Olmsted, John B.   1899, D 19; 1900, Ja 11, F 6, Mr 16

    Jones to Olmsted   1899, D 21; 1900, Ja 12, 18, F 3, 12, Mr 18

Osborn, B. F.   1898, D 8; 1899, Ap 11, My 6

    Jones to Osborn   1898, Mr 28, Ap 15, D 9

Otte, A. F.   1902, Ja 1

    Jones to Otte   1899, My 13, Je 10, 12, 17, 23, Jl 1, 6, 19, 22,
        Ag 3, 8, 26, S 6, 13, 18, 27*; 1900, Mr 21, Ap 4, O 30, N 13, 21,
        D 10; 1901, Ja 5, Mr 20, Je 10, S 11, O 28, N 25; 1902, Ja 17,
        Je 11; 1903, Ja 22, 26, 27, F 12, 16, Mr 23, Ap 29, 30, Je 30,
        Jl 22, N 3

The Outlook Publishing Co.

    Jones to The Outlook Publishing Co.   1898, Mr 25, Ap 12; 1899, Ja 10,
        F 28, Ap 29; 1900, F 12, O 8

Owen, Fred

    Jones to Owen   1901, Jl 18, 30; 1902, Ja 31, My 27, Je 10; 1904,
        My 7, 21

Owen, H. E.   1898, Ag 22, S 13, O 4; 1901, Je 10

    Jones to Owen   1898, Ag 26, S 17, O 12; 1901, Je 7

Packard, C. C.

    Jones to Packard   1897, Je 15, O 8, N 22; 1898, My 13, Je 20, Jl 7;
        1899, My 1, Jl 12, D 27; 1900, Ja 2; 1902, S 27

Page, W. M.   1900, D 29; 1902, Ja 17

    Jones to Page   1898, My 27, Jl 13; 1901, F 8, 13; 1903, F 12

Parker, George

    Jones to Parker   1897, Ag 26; 1899, Mr 9; 1900, F 7, 23,

Parsons, Frank   1898, Jl 16, N 10; 1900, Ap 3, 25; 1901, Ja 12

    Jones to Parsons   1897, Jl 8, D 23; 1898, F 9, 28, Je 27, Jl 9, 28,
        Ag 28, S 14, 17, N 18; 1899, Jl 12, Ag 26, 30, S 6; 1900, My 2;
        1903, D 12; 1904, Ja 22

Peck, Bradford   1900, D 31; 1902, My 23

    Jones to Peck   1900, S 22, N 12, 22; 1901, Ja 3; 1902, My 27, O 30;
        1903, Je 22, 29, Ag 13, D 23

Pelham, (Mrs.) Laura Dainty   1904, My 14

    Jones to Pelham   1899, Ag 4, S 23; 1904, My 19

Perkins, Thomas C.   1901, Ja 1

    Jones to Perkins   1901, Ja 4, 22, F 5, 12

Phillips, Charles H.   1899, D 2

    Jones to Phillips   1899, My 1, Ag 28, D 5

Pingree, Hazen S. (Gov. & Mrs.)   1898, D 27; 1899, Ap 4, Ag 2, O 19, 25

    Jones to Pingree   1897, Ap 21, D 3; 1898, Je 1, S 3, 14, D 15, 29;
        1899, Ja 4, Mr 6, My 9, Je 12, Jl 29, Ag 4, O 18, 23, D 13; 1900,
        F 12, O 12, 20; 1902, Ja 8

Pomeroy, Eltweed (Mr. & Mrs.)   1899, Ap 4; 1900, Ap 3, 14, Ag 22 (folder O);
        1901, Ja 1

    Jones to Pomeroy   1897, N 13, 23; 1898, Je 13, Ag 26, S 21, O 3, N 26,

Pomeroy, Eltweed (Mr. & Mrs.), cont.

        D 16; 1899, Ja 5, 30, F 27, Ap 17, My 10, 22, Je 16, Ag 26, S 6,
        N 11, D 27; 1900, Mr 12, 18, 30, Ap 6, Jl 2, 26, D 21; 1901, N 12,
        D 20; 1903, Ja 13; 1904, My 19

Post, Louis F.   1899, N 10; 1901, Ag 20, O 4

   Jones to Post   1898, Ag 31; 1899, F 6, Ag 5, O 4, N 14, D 4; 1900,
       O 4; 1901, F 5, Ag 17, S 30

Potts, J. D. (See also Eastern Book Concern; Keller & Potts; and Keller, A. R.)
        1899, My 11, Je 27*, S 9, 28, D 7

   Jones to Potts   1899, D 2; 1900, F 8, Jl 18

Pratt, Isaac N.   1899, Mr 26, 31, Ap 4, 22, N 2

   Jones to Pratt   1900, N 6

Priest, R. E.

   Jones to Priest   1901, N 14, D 13; 1902, Mr 31, Ap 23

Radcliffe, Billy   1902, O 2

   Jones to Radcliffe   1899, O 11, 16; 1902, S 30, O 6

Ram's Horn

   Jones to Ram's Horn   1898, My 12, Je 15, Jl 20, N 7, D 7; 1899,
     Jl 14, 21; 1901, Ja 22, S 27

Reardon, Edward M.   1904, Jl 13 (folder FC)

   Jones to Reardon   1897, Jl 6, N 18; 1898, Ja 8; 1901, My 14, Je 20,
     Jl 2, N 13; 1902, Ja 2, 17, 24; 1903, Ag 29; 1904, F 1

Reed, Calvin H.   1901, D 25; 1903, Ja 2

   Jones to Reed   1897, My 11, D 10; 1898, Ja 4, F 15, N 26, D 5; 1899,
     Je 21, Jl 1, D 26; 1900, S 18; 1902, Je 23; 1903, Ja 5; 1904, Ja 21

Riordan, D. M.   1899, Mr 14, Jl 1

   Jones to Riordan   1899, Ap 13, Je 20, Jl 25; 1901, Ap 5; 1902, Ap 7

Rodgers, Edward L.   1899, N 8, D 21, 27; 1900, Ja 6

   Jones to Rodgers   1899, D 22, 28; 1900, Ja 9, Mr 22

Rogers, C. P., Jr.

   Jones to Rogers   1901, Ap 22, My 2, 8, 13, 18, 21, 23, 24, Je 3, 17,
     18, 19, 28, Jl 6, 9, 10, 12, 17, S 4, N 14, 19, D 6, 24; 1902, Ja 4,
     17, Mr 17, 19, Ap 3, N 10, D 2, 8; 1903, Ja 8, F 11, Mr 6

Rouse, S. A.   1900, Ja 21

   Jones to Rouse   1898, Ja 20, F 22, Mr 1, 29, Ap 15; 1900, Ja 24;
       1904, Ja 6

Rudd, R. Graham   1904, Jl 13 (folder FC)

   Jones to Rudd   1897, Ap 23, My 6; 1899, Mr 7, My 5

Rullison, J. E.   1901, Ja 9

   Jones to Rullison   1901, D 31; 1902, Ja 24, My 6; 1903, Jl 2

Russell, L. A.   1900, Jl 14, 26

   Jones to Russell   1899, S 14; 1900, Jl 24

Saul, William   1898, S 18, D 13 (folder O)

   Jones to Saul   1898, S 21, 28, D 19; 1899, Ag 26

Schauss, (Mrs.) Elizabeth   1899, F 21, 24, S 29; 1903, D 25

   Jones to Schauss   1899, F 10, 23; 1900, Ap 20

Scott, George R. and Josephine B.   1903, Jl 14

   Jones to Scott   1897, D 28; 1898, Je 16; 1899, Ap 5; 1902, Jl 8;
       1903, Jl 22, S 11

Scott, Milton R.

   Jones to Scott   1902, F 11, Je 5, O 6, 14; 1903, Ag 4

Seward, Theodore F.   1901, F 7

   Jones to Seward   1897, O 26; 1900, D 7; 1901, My 1, Ag 28, S 9,
       D 17; 1902, F 22

Shaw, Albert   1897, Ap 12; 1899, Ap 4

   Jones to Shaw   1897, My 13; 1899, Ap 11

Sherin, S.   1897, O 8; 1898, Ja 1, F 10, 16, 24, Je 20; 1899, Je 24,
      Jl 7, 19, 22, Ag 2; 1900, Ja 31; 1901, Ap 2

   Jones to Sherin   1897, O 1, 11; 1898, Ja 5, F 11, 21, 22, Mr 16,
      Je 21; 1899, Je 27, Jl 8, 20, Ag 3

Sherwood, Kate Brownlee (Mrs. I. R.)   1900, S 10; 1901, N 1; 1903,
      Ag 31*; [ND]

   Jones to Sherwood   1899, My 3, S 15; 1900, S 17, O 9; 1901, S 16,
      N 6; 1902, O 30, D 23

Sherwood, W. D.

    Jones to Sherwood   1901, Ap 30, Jl 12, 19, 25, S 6, 13, 21,
        O 2, N 5, 9, 14, 16, 27, D 6, 12, 13, 26; 1902, Ja 4, 18, 20, F 7,
        Ap 5, My 3, 21, Je 10, Ag 15, S 22, O 17, 23, N 7, D 16, 30;
        1903, Ja 26, Mr 4, 26

Shuey, E. L.   1898, Ja 4, 10; 1899, Ja 21

    Jones to Shuey   1899, S 11

Simmons, Abram   1898, Ag 24

    Jones to Simmons   1897, D 10; 1898, Ja 4, Ag 26; 1900, Ap 28, D 3

Smallwood, John J. and Rosa E.   1899, My 19; 1903, Ja 29, Mr 3, 11,
        My 7, 20; 1904, Ja 5

    Jones to Smallwood   1899, Ap 17, Je 1, O 2; 1900, F 9, 20, Ap 9,
        O 4, N 6, 24, D 20; 1902, My 22, Je 12, N 7, 10, D 27; 1903, F 9,
        My 11, 22, Ag 19, N 30, D 5; 1904, Ja 8, Ap 25

Smead, Isaac D.

    Jones to Smead   1897, Jl 24; 1898, My 4, Je 25, S 13; 1899, F 25,
        O 2; 1901, F 19, Jl 31

Smith, Don F.

    Jones to Smith   1901, Jl 18, 22, 31, S 4, N 22, D 24; 1902, Ja 29

Soldwedel, Herman R.   1898, Ag 21

    Jones to Soldwedel   1898, Ag 22; 1903, Je 2, 15

Southard, J. H.

    Jones to Southard   1897, S 7; 1898, My 10, D 1; 1903, D 15

Spahr, Charles B.   1898, D 6; 1900, Mr 31, S 19; 1903, Mr 24

    Jones to Spahr   1897, Ap 26; 1898, S 15, D 28; 1900, F 12, Mr 27,
        S 22; 1903, Jl 23

Squire, W. I. and Irving   1900, Ja 18*

    Jones to Squire   1898, My 17, S 13, 22; 1900, Ja 24

Stafford, M. F.   1902, Ja 14; 1903, Ap 7

    Jones to Stafford   1902, Ap 26, Je 3; 1903, Ap 10

Stagge, Lionel   1899, Ap 4*

    Jones to Stagge   1899, Mr 12, Ap 5, Je 8

Steffens, J. Lincoln   1904, Ja 22, Jl 12 and 13 (folder FC)

    Jones to Steffens   1904, Ap 13

Stetson, Charlotte (Perkins) (See Gilman, Charlotte (Perkins) Stetson)

Stevenson, Lewis G.   1900, S 25

    Jones to Stevenson   1900, S 26; 1902, N 25; 1903, Ja 5

Stewart, Jane Agnes   1898, D 21 (folder FC); 1899, N 2

    Jones to Stewart   1898, D 29; 1899, Ja 4

Strickland, Frederick G.   1899, Jl 11, D 6; 1900, Jl 10

    Jones to Strickland   1899, Jl 12; 1902, Ap 30, N 25; 1903, Ja 19

Strobell, George H.   1899, Ap 5

    Jones to Strobell   1900, F 21, Mr 22, S 25

Strong, Josiah   1898, Ag 8; 1899, Ap 6, My 25; 1900, Ja 2; 1901, D 31

    Jones to Strong   1898, Jl 30, Ag 5, 11, S 17, N 15; 1899, Ap 8;
        1900, Ja 30, Je 15; 1901, Ag 15

Taylor, Graham   1897, Ag 28, S 14; 1898, Je 30, S 23; 1899, Ap 3, 4,
        15*; 1900, Ap 5; 1901, Ap 2; 1903, Ap 8; 1904, Jl 12 (folder FC)

    Jones to Taylor   1897, Jl 27; 1898, Ja 26, F 2, Je 24, S 22; 1899,
        Ap 12, Je 5, Ag 15, D 6; 1900, Ag 8, N 23, D 10; 1901, F 4, D 16;
        1902, Jl 14, D 19

Thomas, John H., Family   1904, My 7, Jl 13 (folder FC)

    Jones to Thomas   1897, Je 11; 1899, Mr 18; 1900, Je 11; 1903, Jl 12

Thompson, R. S.   1898, Ag 31, S 9; 1899, F 17, Mr 4, S 28

    Jones to Thompson   1898, S 1; 1899, F 15, 20, Mr 9, Ap 26, My 13,
        S 30

Thurston, L. D.

    Jones to Thurston   1897, Jl 1, O 5, 20, 30; 1898, F 2, Je 9, 13,
        D 16

Tobey, H. A.   1899, Ap 14, D 10

    Jones to Tobey   1897, S 7; 1898, Ap 12*, Jl 1, N 16; 1899, My 9,
        D 11; 1900, Ja 27; 1901, Jl 16

Toledo _Times_

    Jones to Toledo Times   1900, D 24; 1902, D 11, 23; 1903, Je 10

Tolman, William H.   1898, O 5; 1899, O 30

    Jones to Tolman   1898, N 8; 1899, D 11; 1903, D 30

Traubel, Horace L.   1899, My 22, Je 30; 1901, My 17, Je 19, 26; 1902,
       Ja [?], Mr 2, Ap 9, 13, 25, My 14, 16, 20*, 25, Je 23, Jl 8, 9,
       10, 11, 18, 19, 20, 21, 22, 23, 25, 26, 27, 28, 29, 30, 31, Ag 1,
       3, 4, 5, 6, 7, 8, 9, 10, 11, 13, 14, 20, 26, 27, S 13, 19, 24,
       O 2, 15, 27, D 12, 20; 1903, F 23, Mr 19, 20, 22, 23, Ap 2, 7,
       11, 23, 30, My 12, 20*, 23, Je 2, Ag 17, S 4, O 16, N 15, D 27;
       1904, Ap 14, 20, My 23

    Jones to Traubel   1899, My 26; 1900, My 10; 1901, My 14, 21, 27,
       Je 21, Ag 17, S 9, 25, N 29*; 1902, Ja 4, Ap 3, 10, 22, My 16,
       22, S 8, 11, 26, O 6, 28, D 8, 15; 1903, Mr 21, Ap 7, 29, My 18,
       22, 29, Ag 13, O 19, D 1, 30; 1904, Ap 18, My 28

Trine, Ralph Waldo   1899, S 12

    Jones to Trine   1899, S 15; 1900, Ja 10, My 15

Tsanoff, Stoyan Vasil   1899, Ap 26

    Jones to Tsanoff   1899, My 22, Je 7; 1901, N 22

Tucker, Fred H.   1900, Ja 5; 1903, F 9

    Jones to Tucker   1899, D 19, 22; 1902, F 22; 1903, F 12

Tuckerman, Gustavus   1898, My 3; 1900, Ja 1, Jl 2

    Jones to Tuckerman   1898, Ap 30, S 16; 1900, Jl 7

Upton, (Mrs.) Harriet Taylor   1903, Jl 9, 22

    Jones to Upton   1901, D 6; 1903, Ja 27, Jl 14

Voiles, W. R.   1899, My 7

    Jones to Voiles   1899, My 1, 9, 13, Je 23, Jl 12, Ag 7, 26, 29,
       S 1

Waggoner, Clark   1897, Mr 6, 10, 11, 18, Ap 6

Waldorf, George P.   1897, Jl 21; 1899, Mr 11

    Jones to Waldorf   1897, Jl 21; 1899, Mr 7, O 11

Walker, John Brisben   1899, Mr 30

    Jones to Walker   1899, F 1, Mr 13, Ap 1, 8, Jl 19, 29; 1900,

Walker, John Brisben, cont.

  Ja 11; <u>1901</u>, My 13; <u>1902</u>, Ap 15

Walker, W. S.

  <u>Jones to Walker</u>   <u>1899</u>, My 9, Ag 3, S 8; <u>1900</u>, S 25

Walton, Arthur T.

  <u>Jones to Walton</u>   <u>1901</u>, My 16, D 20; <u>1902</u>, Ja 4, N 10; <u>1903</u>, Ja 9,
        20, Ap 3, N 5

Weeks, Rufus W.   <u>1899</u>, Mr 28, O 11

  <u>Jones to Weeks</u>   <u>1897</u>, O 27; <u>1899</u>, Ap 1, My 9, S 27, O 16

Wentworth, Franklin H.   <u>1899</u>, D 8, 30; <u>1900</u>, Mr 5, 9, Ap 13, D 26

  <u>Jones to Wentworth</u>   <u>1898</u>, O 13; <u>1899</u>, S 7, 12, 18, O 4, D 11; <u>1900</u>,
        Ja 9, Mr 21, My 4, Je 12, Ag 13, 24, D 4; <u>1901</u>, F 20, My 22, N 8,
        16; <u>1902</u>, S 30, O 10; <u>1903</u>, Mr 6, 9; <u>1904</u>, Mr 7, 16

Wheelock, Edwin D.   <u>1897</u>, D 3; <u>1898</u>, Ja 11, 22, F 14, 22, 26, S 6, 13,
        22, O 31; <u>1899</u>, Ap 4, S 27, N 16, 18, 20; <u>1900</u>, F 1, Mr 14, Jl 10;
        <u>1903</u>, Ap 7

  <u>Jones to Wheelock</u>   <u>1898</u>, Ja 12, 26, F 2, 16, 21, 25, 28, Je 6, Ag 12,
        S 8, 17, 23, O 19, N 7, D 8, 15; <u>1899</u>, Mr 9, Je 10, O 2, 11, N 17,
        21; <u>1900</u>, Mr 23, Jl 14, S 26, O 29, 30, N 21, 27, D 24; <u>1901</u>, O 31;
        <u>1904</u>, My 19

White, J. W.   <u>1899</u>, Ap 4

  <u>Jones to White</u>   <u>1897</u>, My 1, 3, 14, 17, Jl 2, Ag 13, 20, S 10, 21,
        O 20, 28, N 1, 22, D 21; <u>1898</u>, Ja 12, 26, F 7, 9, 16, 23, Ap 26,
        28, My 3, 5, 16, 17, 27, Je 16, 27, Jl 13, Ag 8, 26, S 15, O 12,
        N 17, 25; <u>1899</u>, F 27, Mr 3, 14, Ap 3*, 17, Je 27, N 27; <u>1900</u>, F 21,
        Mr 12, Je 20, Jl 18; <u>1901</u>, F 1, My 21, N 19; <u>1902</u>, Ja 29

Whitlock, Brand   <u>1904</u>, Jl 2 (folder FC)

  <u>Jones to Whitlock</u>   <u>1901</u>, D 31; <u>1902</u>, Ap 7, Jl 27, Ag 2; <u>1903</u>, Ag 30;
        <u>1904</u>, Ap 15

Will, Thomas E.   <u>1900</u>, Ja 15, Ap 4, Je 8, Jl 11, 19

  <u>Jones to Will</u>   <u>1899</u>, Jl 19; <u>1900</u>, Ja 18, My 17, Je 11, Jl 20

Willis, E. B.   <u>1899</u>, S 29, N 3

  <u>Jones to Willis</u>   <u>1898</u>, N 17; <u>1899</u>, O 3

Wilshire, H. Gaylord

    <u>Jones to Wilshire</u>   <u>1899</u>, S 13; <u>1901</u>, F 11; <u>1902</u>, N 10; <u>1904</u>, Mr 10

Wilson, J. Stitt   <u>1900</u>, Je 26; <u>1901</u>, Ap 12, My 29; <u>1903</u>, Ap 7

    <u>Jones to Wilson</u>   <u>1899</u>, S 6, N 17; <u>1900</u>, Je 28, Jl 3, 19, 27, Ag 6,
        N 8; <u>1901</u>, Ap 1, My 23, Jl 26

Witt, Peter   <u>1903</u>, Ap 7

    <u>Jones to Witt</u>   <u>1899</u>, S 11, O 2, 3; <u>1900</u>, Ag 24

Wood, Tom J.

    <u>Jones to Wood</u>   <u>1901</u>, Ja 21, 24; <u>1902</u>, Ja 14; <u>1903</u>, Ja 26, D 5

Woodruff, Clinton Rogers   <u>1898</u>, O 22 (folder O); <u>1899</u>, Ap 10; <u>1900</u>,
        D 31

    <u>Jones to Woodruff</u>   <u>1898</u>, Ag 31, N 17, 23, D 9, 20; <u>1899</u>, F 14, Ap 13,
        Jl 11, Ag 22; <u>1902</u>, F 26; <u>1903</u>, S 24; <u>1904</u>, Ja 5, Mr 14, Jl 8

Young, W. S.

    <u>Jones to Young</u>   <u>1899</u>, O 3, 12; <u>1902</u>, Je 17, S 23; <u>1903</u>, Ap 11

Young, Walter L.   <u>1899</u>, Ap 4, Jl 13*

    <u>Jones to Young</u>   <u>1897</u>, D 8; <u>1898</u>, Ja 8, Ap 25, D 6; <u>1899</u>, Jl 19;
        <u>1901</u>, Jl 24; <u>1902</u>, F 14, Ap 2, 22*, O 16, N 20; <u>1903</u>, Je 15, Ag 11,
        S 1, 28, D 2; <u>1904</u>, Ja 6, F 15, Mr 15, Ap 25

Zeigler, Henry C.

    <u>Jones to Zeigler</u>   <u>1897</u>, Jl 14; <u>1898</u>, Jl 16; <u>1899</u>, Mr 17; <u>1901</u>, My 21

Zueblin, Charles

    <u>Jones to Zueblin</u>   <u>1900</u>, Ap 27, My 17, 31; <u>1901</u>, Ja 30, N 21, D 28

Writings by Samuel M. Jones

SPEECHES AND ARTICLES

DATE	PLACE	TITLE	PAGES & FORM
[Dec. 1896]	Toledo	"Eight-Hour Day in the Oil Regions"	8pp Pamphlet
Feb. 1897 - Mar. 26, 1898	Toledo	"Donaldson Correspondence" [Exchange of Letters Between Jones and the Toledo Clergy]	5pp T
[Feb.-Apr. 4, 1897]	Toledo	[Address Before Republican Gathering Concerning the Mayoral Campaign 1897]	4pp T
Mch. 23, 1897	Toledo	"National and Municipal Politics, an Address Before the 14th Ward Jackson League Club"	15pp T
Apr. 24, 1897	Toledo	[Address at First City Department Heads Meeting]	2pp T
[May 20, 1897]	Toledo	[Caption for "Divide the Day" in Toledo Blade]	4pp T
[May 25, 1897]	Toledo	"Welcome to Knights of Pythias"	2pp T
May 25, 1897	Toledo	[Address on Secret Societies to Knights of Pythias Convention]	2pp T
[July 16, 1897]	[Toledo]	[Address to the Reunion of the 100th Ohio Volunteer Infantry]	1p T
Aug. 23, 1897	Toledo	"Address to the Deutsch Amerikanische Kriegerbund"	2pp T
Sept. 24, 1897	Toledo	"Welcome to the Men of the City of Detroit"	1p T

```
Forms:  T = typed
        P = printed
        A = autographed
```

[Sept.-Oct. 1897]	Toledo	[Golden Rule Park Address]	2pp T
Oct. 16, 1897	[Toledo]	[Contract Labor]	1p T
Oct. 26, 1897	Toledo	"Address of Welcome to the 7th Annual Ohio State Conference of Charities and Correction"	4pp P
Nov. 24, 1897	Toledo	"Patriotism - What Is It? An Address Before the Current Topic Club, Epworth Church"	5pp T
[Nov. 25, 1897]	[Toledo]	[Thanksgiving]	1p T
Christmas, 1897	Toledo	"To the Workers of the Acme Oil Company	1p P
[1897]	Toledo	[Address Before the Ohio State Sunday School Convention]	4pp T
[June 23, 1898]	[Toledo]	[Address to Grocers and Butchers]	2pp T
[May-Aug. 1898]	[Toledo]	[Address to Toledo Police Force]	3pp T
Aug. 3, 1898	Detroit	[Municipal Ownership: An Address Before the League of American Municipalities]	10pp T
Sept. 8, 1898	[n. p.]	"Prostitution"	4pp T
Sept. 12, 1898	Toledo	[A Municipal Gas Plant: An Address to City Council]	3pp T
[Oct. 24, 1898]	Toledo	[A Municipal Gas Plant: A Message to City Council]	2pp T
Nov. 8, 1898	Toledo	"The New Right"	4pp T
		"The New Right" as published in The Independent, Dec. 29, 1898	3pp P
[Nov. 22, 1898]	[St. Louis, Mo.]	"Our Brothers, the Millionaire and the Tramp"	5pp T
Dec. 21, 1898	Toledo	[New Year's Greeting]	1p T
[Jan. 16, 1899]	[New York City]	"What Should the City Own? A Municipal Ownership Address"	26pp T

[Jan. 1899]	[Toledo]	[Acme Sucker Rod Company: The Economic and Social Conditions Which Influenced Its Business Philosophy]	8pp T
Feb. 6, 1899	Toledo	[Mayoral Campaign 1899 - Municipal Issues: A Question and Answer Presentation]	6pp T
Feb. 7, 1899	Toledo	"The New Right and How To Obtain It"	5pp T
[Mar. 1899]	[Toledo]	"Opening of the Campaign of Education"	2pp T
May 11, 1899	Toledo	[Republican Primaries 1899: Statement Declaring Non-Candidacy for Governor]	1p T
[ca. May 18, 1899]	[n. p.]	[Preliminary Draft of "Charity or Justice, Which?"]	6pp T
May 18, 1899	Cincinnati, O.	"Charity or Justice, Which?" - (An Address Before the National Convention of Charities and Correction)	9pp T
June 10 [1899]	St. Louis, Mo.	"The Business Administration of a City"	9 pp T
June 19, 1899	Cincinnati, O.	"The Labor Question: An Address to a Mass Meeting of Workingmen at Cincinnati Music Hall" [Written Toledo, May 15, 1899]	11pp T
June 21, 1899	Toledo	[Message to People of Toledo Concerning a City-Owned Gas Plant]	3pp T
June 22, 1899	Cleveland, O.	"Principle Before Party: An Address Before the Central Labor Union"	2pp T
[June 1899]	[n. p.]	[Preliminary Notes for "The New Education"]	3pp A
[June 1899]	[Grinnell, Iowa]	"The New Education" (Commencement Address at Grinnell College)	5pp T
June 1899	Toledo	"Municipal Expansion" as published in the Arena, June 1899	2pp P

July 1, 1899	Pittsburgh, Pa.	"Mayor Jones' Speech" (At Invitation of Organized Labor)	5pp T (Incomplete)
[July 5, 1899]	Toledo	[Address to Christian Endeavorers]	3pp T
July 26, 1899	Toledo	"Opening of the Children's Playground"	2pp T
July 29, 1899	Toledo	"To the People of Ohio" - [A Statement Concerning Jones' Willingness to Be a Gubernatorial Condidate]	2pp T
July 29, 1899	Toledo	"To the People of Ohio" [Published Version of Above]	1p P
Aug. 8, 1899	Toledo	"The Opening of the Centennial Carnival"	1p T
Aug. 8, 1899	Toledo	"Open Letter to the People of Ohio During the Non-Partisan Campaign"	3pp T
Aug. 9, 1899	Cleveland, O.	"Municipal Ownership: The Final Remedy for Street Railway Strikes" (Address Before Strikers' Picnic, Scenic Park, Cleveland)	3pp T
[Aug. 26, 1899]	[Toledo]	"To the People of Ohio" (A Statement of Acceptance of Nomination as Non-Partisan Candidate for Governor)	4pp T
Aug. 31, 1899	Toledo	"Labor Day Greeting"	1p T
[ca.Aug. 1899]	[n. p.]	"Hints and Suggestions to Speakers and Workers in the Non-Partisan Cause"	2pp T
[ca.Aug. 1899]	[n. p.]	"A Lesson from a Great Trust"	4pp T
[Aug. 1899]	[n. p.]	"The Failure of Success and the Success of Failure"	17pp T
[Aug.-Nov. 1899]	[n. p.]	"To the Workers in the Non-Partisan Cause"	1p T
Sept. 4, 1899	Columbus, O.	"Labor Day Address"	4pp T
Sept. 6-11, 1899	[n. p.]	"To the Friends of the Non-Partisan Movement"	3pp T

Sept. 14, 1899	Toledo	"To the Order of the Woodmen of the World"	2pp T
[Sept. 16, 1899]	[Toledo]	"The Race Problem"	3pp T
Sept. 1899	[n. p.]	"The New Patriotism: A Golden Rule Government for Cities" as published in Municipal Affairs, Sept. 1899	7pp P
[Oct. 7, 1899]	[Toledo]	"Mayor Jones Platform"	1p T
Oct. 10, 1899	Toledo	"The Piracy of Business"	4pp T
Oct. 18, 1899	Toledo	"Non-Partisan Political Action the Only Way to Political Freedom"	1p T (Incomplete)
[Nov. 8, 1899]	[Toledo]	["Great Desecration and Great Victory"] "Mayor Jones to Cuyahoga County" an article sent to the Cincinnati Post	1p T
[Dec. 1899]	[Toledo]	"Outline for a Supplementary Chapter on Non-Partisan Politics"	6pp T
[1899]	[Toledo]	"Memorial Hall Address on Pipe Line"	7pp T
[1899?]	[n. p.]	"The Golden Rule in Real Life"	9pp T
Jan. 16-18, 1900	Dayton, O.	"Municipal Ownership According to the Proposed New Municipal Code - An Address to the League of Ohio Municipalities"	6pp T
Feb. 6, 1900	Toledo	[Non-Partisan Politics and Direct Legislation]	1p T
[Feb. 7, 1900]	Toledo	"The Religious Condition of the Working Men in America at the Close of the 19th Century"	4pp T
1900		"The Religious Condition of the Working Men in America at the Close of the 19th Century" as published in Morgan, J. Vyrnwy, Theology at the Dawn of the 20th Century	6pp T
Feb. 13, 1900	Chicago, Ill.	"An Address delivered at the Anti-Trust Conference"	7pp T
Mar. 17, 1900	St. Louis, Mo.	"Response to the Toast, the Cymric Celts - An Address to the Knights of St. Patrick"	5pp T

[Mar. 18, 1900]	[Toledo]	"Education" (Jones' comments as one of the editors of <u>Complete Education</u>)	2pp T
Mar. 22, 1900	Toledo	"Non-Partisan Politics in Ohio"	1p T
Mar. 31, 1900	Toledo	"Money Making"	1p T
Apr. 6, 1900	Toledo	"Socialist or What?"	1p T
Apr. 11, 1900	Chicago, Ill.	"The Golden Rule" (Address Before the Woman's Club)	6pp T
[ca.April 1900]	[n. p.]	"The Golden Rule"	4pp T
Apr. 24 [1900]	Boston, Mass.	"The Religious Motive in Political Life" (Address Before the Congress of Religions)	3pp T
[Apr. 25, 1900]	[Troy, N.Y.]	"Why I Am a Non-Partisan" (Under Auspices of Central Federation of Labor)	8pp T
Apr. 28, 1900	Toledo	"Contract and Day Labor Plan"	1p T
[May 12, 1900]	Toledo	"Equality: From <u>Letters of Labor and Love</u>" as published in <u>Craftsman</u>, November 1905	1p P (Incomplete)
May 22, 1900	Toledo	"The Way to Get Rid of the Party Boss"	2pp T
June 5, 1900	Toledo	"Beginning the Boulevard Work"	2pp T
June 19, 1900	Toledo	"Socialism and Equality" (As Written for the <u>Socialist Review</u>, Kearney, Nebraska)	2pp T
June 20, 1900	Toledo	"Address Before the Grammar School Graduates"	3pp T
June 30, 1900	Toledo	"Address to Toledo Police Force at Annual Inspection"	2pp T (Incomplete)
June 30, 1900 [?]	Toledo	"Address at Annual Inspection of Toledo Police Department"	4pp P
July 7, 1900	Toledo	"What Can Woman Do Toward Good City Government?"	3pp T
July 13, 1900	Toledo	"Public Ownership the Only Cure for Trusts, Strikes, Government by Injunction and Government by the Sword"	5pp T

July 14, 1900		"American Workingmen and Religion" as published in <u>Outlook</u>, July 24, 1900	3pp P
July 31, 1900	Toledo	"An Address of Welcome to the Democratic Clubs of Ohio"	3pp T
Aug. 1, 1900	Toledo	"Home"	2pp T
Aug. 7, 1900	Toledo	"How Shall We Apply the Principles of Christianity to the Affairs of the National Government?"	2pp T
Sept. 4, 1900	[Toledo]	"Labor Day Address at Presque Isle (At Invitation of Building Trades Council)	6pp T (Incomplete)
Sept. 5, 1900	Columbus O.	"Non-Partisan Conference, State House Steps, Columbus"	3pp T
Sept. 13, 1900	Toledo	"My Political Attitude"	3pp T
Sept. 20, 1900	Toledo	"Address at the Democratic Congressional Convention"	2pp T
Sept. 30 [1900]	Toledo	"Infidelity the Only National Danger"	9pp T
Oct. 13, 1900	Akron, O.	"An Appeal to Patriotism: The Right of Self Government"	4pp T
[Oct. 1900]	[n. p.]	"Christianity and War"	2pp T
Nov. 4, 1900	[Cleveland, O.]	"Sunday Politics and Weekday Religion"	4pp T
Dec. 31, 1900	Toledo	"Visions of the 20th Century" an Address at the Citizens Watch Meeting	2pp T
[ca. Jan. 20, 1901]	Toledo	"Non-Partisan Politics" as published in the <u>Denver</u> [Colo.] <u>Times</u>	4pp T
Jan. 1901	Toledo	"Twentieth Century Greetings of the Acme Sucker Rod Co."	2pp T
Feb. 4, 1901	Buffalo, N.Y.	"Problems of Industrialism"	4pp T
Feb. 23, 1901	Toledo	"A Talk to the Boys at Memorial Hall"	2pp T

Mar. 9, [1901]	Toledo	"Trade Unionism" as published in <u>Letters of Love and Labor</u>, Vol. 2	2pp T
Mar. 14, 1901	Toledo	"Aristocracy or Democracy"	3pp T
April 1, 1901	Toledo	"Advice to High School Graduates" as published in <u>Ann Arbor High School "Omega" 1901</u>	2pp P
May 18, 1901	[Toledo]	"An Address on Peace"	3pp T
May 1901	Toledo	"Patience and Education the Demands of the Hour" as published in <u>The Arena</u>, May 1901	3pp P
June 6, 1901	[Toledo]	"The New Education: An Address to the Graduates of the Misses Law's Kindergarten Training School"	10pp T
July 8, 1901	Toledo	"An Address of Welcome to the Longshoremen's Union"	3pp T
July 9, 1901	Toledo	"How the Golden Rule Was Made Conspicuous in Toledo"	4pp T
[Aug. 30, 1901]	[n. p.]	"Are the Interests of Employer and Employed Mutual?"	3pp T
1902		"Socialism and Single Tax: Equality and Co-Operation" [Another form of "Are the Interests of Employer and Employed Mutual?"] as published in <u>Labor and Capital: A Discussion of the Relations of Employer and Employed</u>, edited by John P. Peters, 1902	3pp P
Sept. 1, 1901	Toledo	"Address of Welcome to the Swiss Saengerfest"	2pp T
Sept. 7, 1901	Toledo	[The Assualt Upon President McKinley]	2pp T
[Oct. 11, 1901]	[Toledo]	[Introductory Remarks at a Horse Race]	1p T
Oct. 25, 1901	[Lima, Ohio]	"What is Crime and Who Are the Criminals?" delivered Before the Board of State Charities of Ohio	5pp T
Oct. 25, 1901	Lima, Ohio	Pamphlet Copy of Preceding Entry	12pp Pamphlet

[ca. Oct. 1901]	[Detroit, Mich.]	"Are Political Parties Necessary, or Are They Obstacles to Political Progress?"	3pp T
Nov. 9, 1901	Toledo	"One Day's Experience in the Mayor's Office and Some of Its Lessons"	3pp T
Nov. 26, 1901	Toledo	"What Toledo Has to be Thankful For"	1p T
[1901]	[n. p.]	"The Responsibilities of Citizenship"	2pp T
[ca. Jan. 1902]	[n. p.]	"The Business of Politics"	3pp T
Feb. 6, 1902	Columbus, O.	"What is Crime and Who Are the Criminals?" delivered to League of Ohio Municipalities, February 6, 1902	6pp T
Feb. 27, 1902	Toledo	"The Way to Purify Politics"	2pp P
Feb. 27, 1902	Toledo	[An Address to Acme Sucker Rod Employees Before Leaving for Texas]	6pp T
Apr. 3, 1902	Toledo	"To the People of Toledo" [Concerning the Bill Designed to Deprive Cities of Home Rule]	2pp T
Apr. 12, 1902	Toledo	"Work and Education"	3pp T
Apr. 19, 1902	Toledo	"An Address to the Toledo Police Force, Annual Inspection"	3pp T
Apr. 23, 1902	Toledo	"Address at Opening of Base Ball Season"	1p T
Apr. 24, 1902	Toledo	"Is the Golden Rule Practical?"	3pp T
Apr. 25, 1902	Toledo	"Concerning the Finances of the Golden Rule Dining Hall"	2pp T
May 3, 1902	Toledo	"The Police Board Question" Written for the Courier-Journal	3pp T
June 8, 1902	Toledo	"Speech at 6th Annual Opening of Golden Rule Park"	7pp T
June 17, 1902	Toledo	"The Successful American"	2pp T

June 18, 1902	Toledo	"The Boys' Industrial School at Lancaster, Ohio"	4pp T
June 27, 1902	Toledo	[State Supreme Court Decision Declaring the Legislation Concerning the Police Board Unconstitutional]	3pp T
[July 1902]	[Toledo]	"The Working People" written for The American Federationist	28pp A
	[Toledo]	"The Working People" written for The American Federationist	3pp T
Aug. 3, 1902	Toledo	"Hospitality" written for the Toledo Blade	12pp T
	Toledo	"Hospitality" written for the Toledo Blade	2pp T
Aug. 27, 1902	Grand Rapids, Mich.	"What is Crime and Who Are the Criminals?" delivered to League of American Municipalities, August 27, 1902	28pp T
[Oct. 15, 1902]	Peoria, Ill.	"Address at Presentation of Columbus Monument to City of Peoria"	4pp T
Nov. 5, 1902	Toledo	"Partyism" written for the Chicago Record-Herald	4pp T
Dec. 21, 1902	Chicago	"Address Before Peace Society"	6pp T
Dec. 25, 1902	Toledo	"A Christmas Message from Samuel M. Jones to the Workingmen of the Acme Sucker Rod Co. and All Others Who Care to Read It"	24pp Pamphlet
[Jan. 1] 1903	Toledo	"1903 Love's Day"	1p Card
Jan. 22, 1903	Toledo	"The Development of a Pure Democracy"	3pp T
Jan. 23, 1903	[Toledo]	"Why Don't You Marry the Girl? We'll Help You." Sent to Arena	2pp T
	Toledo	"A Plea for Simpler Living" (An Enlargement of the Preceding Topic) as published in Arena, April 1903	4pp P

Jan. 1903	[Toledo]	"Government by the Golden Rule" as published in <u>Munsey's Magazine</u>, January 1903	4pp P
Feb. 18, 1903	Toledo	"The Power of the Press"	2pp T
May 17, 1903	Toledo	"The Golden Rule in Business" delivered at First Congregational Sunday School	5pp T
June 25, 1903	Toledo	"The Non-Partisan in Politics"	9pp T
	Toledo	"The Non-Partisan in Politics" as published in <u>The Independent</u>, August 20, 1903	4pp P
[June 1903]	[Toledo]	"A Page from Experience" (A Contribution to <u>The Public Trust</u>, Charles Ferguson's Magazine)	3pp T
Oct. 8, 1903	Baltimore, Md.	"The Ideal American" delivered to League of American Municipalities	14pp T
Nov. 28, 1903	Toledo	"A Southern Prison Farm"	5pp T
[Nov. 29, 1903]	[Chicago, Ill.]	[Tribute to Henry Demarest Lloyd]	2pp T
Dec. 25, 1903	Toledo	"A Christmas Message About 'Man' in Song and Prose"	19pp Pamphlet
[1903]	[n. p.]	"Success for Young Men"	5pp T (Incomplete)
[1903]	[n. p.]	[On Punishment] as published in Lewis, Fay. <u>The City Jail</u>, 1903	3pp P
Feb. 29, 1904	Toledo	[Remarks at Marriage Service for Minnie C. Ballert and George Shetley]	4pp T
Mar. 20, 1904	Toledo	"The Drunkenness of Luxury"	13pp T
Apr. 1, 1904	[Toledo]	"Marriage Service of Robert Waugh and Virginia Horcher"	2pp T
[1904]	[n. p.]	"The Vice of Luxury"	3pp T (Unfinished)

UNDATED SPEECHES AND ARTICLES

[n. d.]	[n. p.]	"Anecdotes and Stories"	1p T
[Labor Day]	[n. p.]	"The Art Idea as Associated with Labor"	2pp T
[n. d.]	[n. p.]	"Capital Punishment"	3pp T
[n. d.]	[n. p.]	[Civic Patriotism]	5pp T
[n. d.]	[n. p.]	"The Crusade Against Vice in New York and Chicago"	1p T
[n. d.]	[n. p.]	"Education and 'Business Success'"	1p T
[n. d.]	Toledo	[Elks: Address Before the Benevolent and Protective Order of Elks]	5pp T (Incomplete)
[Feb.]	[Toledo]	"The Failure of Punishment"	3pp T
[Dec. 25,]	[Toledo]	"The Larger Christmas"	2pp T
[n. d.]	[Toledo]	[Letter to the Editor of the Toledo Blade on "A Man Who Has Grown Rich"]	3pp A
[n. d.]	[n. p.]	"The New Municipal Code"	4pp T
[n. d.]	[n. p.]	"The New Ohio Code"	3pp T
[n. d.]	Boston, Mass.	"Parker Memorial" Speech	7pp T
[n. d.]	[n. p.]	[Proclamation of Mourning]	1p T
[n. d.]	[n. p.]	"The Religion of the Shorter Work-Day"	1p T
[n. d.]	[n. p.]	"Social and Industrial Questions"	4pp T
[n. d.]	[n. p.]	"The Socialist Colony Movement"	1p T
[n. d.]	[Toledo]	[Typical Morning in My Job]	1p T
[n. d.]	Toledo	[Welcome Address to the Bicycle Workers at Presque Isle]	3pp T

[n. d.]	[Toledo]	[Welcome Message at the Children's Paper Picnic]	1p T
[n. d.]	[Toledo]	"The Wrong of the License System of Raising Revenue"	2pp T

ADDENDUM

[July 2, 1903]	Toledo	"The Mayor of Toledo is a Thorough Physical Culturist" as published in Physical Culture, Sept. 1903	3pp P

MAYOR'S MESSAGES TO TOLEDO COMMON COUNCIL

Jan. 3, 1898	First Annual Message	Pamphlet	15pp
Oct. 24 & 26, 1898	Second Annual Message and 2 Page Supplementary of October 26	Pamphlet	31pp
Aug. 14, 1899	Third Annual Message	Printed	21pp
[n. d.]	Fourth Annual Message	Pamphlet	32pp
Feb. 24, 1902	Fifth Annual Message	Pamphlet	16pp
Mch. 2 & 17, 1903	Sixth Annual Message With Supplement Containing Jones' Letter of Acceptance of Nomination, March 17	Pamphlet	20pp

PUBLISHED VOLUMES BY SAMUEL MILTON JONES

The New Right: A Plea for Fair Play Through a More Just Social Order. New York: Eastern Book Concern, 1899; Westport, Conn: Hyperion Press, Reprint 1976.

Letters of Love and Labor. vol. 1. Toledo, Ohio: Franklin Printing & Engraving Co., 1900.

Letters of Love and Labor. vol. 2. Toledo, Ohio: Franklin Printing & Engraving Co., 1901.

Letters of Labor and Love. Reprint (2 vols. in 1). Indianapolis:
    Bobbs-Merrill Co., 1905.

SONGS AND POETRY BY SAMUEL MILTON JONES

"Divide the Day"   Words and Music   4pp Published
                                        Copyright, May 26, 1897

"Freedom's Day"   1898 Golden Rule Park   Ribbon
                                        Opening

"Industrial Freedom"   Feb. 10, 1899   1p P

"God Pity the Idlers"   Sept. 2, 1901   3pp A

"God Pity the Idlers"   Sept. 2, 1901   1p P

"God Pity the Idlers"   Sept. 2, 1901   1p P

"God Pity the Idlers"   Sept. 7, 1903   Ribbon

"No Title is Higher Than Man"   [n. d.]   2pp

"Freedom Songs": "Freedom Day"   [n. d.]   2pp P
and "Promise" and discourse on
"Faith in Humanity"

"Freedom Songs": "Divide the Day",   [1897 - 1901]   2pp P
"Industrial Freedom", "The Man
Without a Party", "Freedom Day"
and "Promise"

"Freedom Songs": "Industrial   [n. d.]   2pp P
Freedom" and "The Man Without
a Party"

Related Materials

The following bibliography contains the major books, pamphlets, and magazine articles concerning the career of Samuel M. Jones. As publications containing references to the mayor are too numerous to list here, researchers are advised to consult also the holdings of the Toledo-Lucas County Library, Local History Department. Significant materials not included in this bibliography are: genealogical data, newspaper articles, correspondence resulting from the project, and the extensive research materials compiled by the processor.

BOOKS AND ARTICLES

Baker, Newton D. Introduction to *The Letters and Journal of Brand Whitlock*, edited by Allan Nevins. New York and London: D. Appleton-Century Co., 1936.

Bremner, Robert H. "The Civic Revival in Ohio: The Fight Against Privilege in Cleveland and Toledo 1899-1912." Ph.D. dissertation, Ohio State University, 1943.

_____. "Samuel M. Jones: The Man Without a Party." *American Journal of Economics and Sociology* 8 (1949):150-161.

Carlton, Frank T. "The Golden-Rule Factory: The Late Mayor Jones' Contribution Toward the Solution of Industrial Problems." *The Arena* 32 (1904): 408-410.

Casson, Herbert N. "Draining a Political Swamp." *The Arena* 21 (1899):768-772.

Chamberlain, John. *Farewell to Reform*. New York: Liveright, Inc., Publishers, 1932.

Crosby, Ernest. "Golden-Rule Jones, the Late Mayor of Toledo." *The Craftsman* 7 (1904-5):530.

_____. *Golden Rule Jones, Mayor of Toledo*. Chicago: Public Publishing Company, [1906.]

Crunden, Robert M. *A Hero in Spite of Himself: Brand Whitlock in Art, Politics, & War*. New York: Alfred A. Knopf, 1969.

Cumulative Book Review Digest. 1 (1905):195.

"Death of a Philanthropist." *Brotherhood of Locomotive Firemen's Magazine*

37 (1904):261-262.

Dictionary of American Biography. vol. 21 Supplement 1. New York: Charles Scribner's Sons, 1944. 453-454.

"Divide the Day." *Toledo Critic* 8 (April 2, 1898):21-23.

Downes, Randolph C. *Industrial Beginnings.* Lucas County Historical Series, vol. 4. Toledo, Ohio: The Historical Society of Northwestern Ohio, 1954.

_____. "Jones and Whitlock and the Promotion of Urban Democracy." *Northwest Ohio Quarterly* 28 (1955-56):26-37.

_____. "Watered Securities and the Independent Revolution in Toledo Politics, 1901-1907." *Northwest Ohio Quarterly* 28 (1956):103.

Effler, Louis R. *My Memoirs of the Gay 90's.* Toledo, Ohio: Buettner & Breska, 1942.

Ekirch, Arthur A., Jr. *Progressivism in America: A Study of the Era from Theodore Roosevelt to Woodrow Wilson.* New York: Franklin Watts, Inc., New Viewpoints, 1974.

Elsesser, William J. *A Study of the Social Ideas of Samuel M. Jones.* Toledo, Ohio: University of Toledo, 1967.

Fess, Simeon D. *Ohio, A Four Volume Reference Library.* vol. 4. Chicago and New York: Lewis Publishing Co., 1937.

Filler, Louis. *Crusaders for American Liberalism.* Yellow Springs, Ohio: Antioch Press, 1950.

Ford, Harvey S. "The Diary of John Beatty." *Ohio State Archaeological and Historical Quarterly* 58 (1949):126-128.

_____. "The Life and Times of Golden Rule Jones." Ph.D. dissertation, University of Michigan, 1953. Microfilm.

Frederick, Peter J. *Knights of the Golden Rule: The Intellectual as Christian Social Reformer in the 1890s.* Lexington, Ky.: University Press of Kentucky, 1976.

Gavit, John Palmer. "Of the Dear Love of Comrades." *Commons* 9 (1904): 358-359.

Gilman, Nicholas Paine. "The Acme Sucker Rod Company, of Toledo, Ohio." In *A Dividend to Labor: A Study of Employers' Welfare Institution.* Boston and New York: Houghton, Mifflin and Co., 1899. 234.

Glaab, Charles. *The American City: A Documentary History.* Homewood, Ill., Dorsey Press, 1963.

Gladden, George, ed. "Current Discussion — Both Sides." *Current Literature* 37 (1904):201.

Gladden, Washington. "Mayor Jones of Toledo." *The Outlook* 62 (May 6, 1899): 17-21.

"'Golden Rule' Jones of Toledo." *The American Monthly Review of Reviews* 30 (1904):354-355.

"The 'Golden Rulers' of Toledo." *Literary Digest* 46 (1913):797-801.

Goll, Ralph. "Petermen's Saint." *Esquire* 11 (June 1939):58.

History of Lewis County, New York 1880-1965. Edited by G. Byron Bowen. Board of Legislators of Lewis County, N.Y., 1970.

Hope, Derrill. "The Golden Rule in Toledo." *Social Gospel* 39 (May 1901): 7-11.

Howe, Frederic C. *Confessions of a Reformer.* New York: Charles Scribner's Sons, 1925.

Hubbard, Elbert. "Golden Rule Jones." *The Philistine* 19 (September 1904): 105-121.

_____. *Little Journeys to the Homes of Good Men and Great.* Memorial ed. vol. 4. East Aurora, N.Y.: The Roycrofters, and New York and Chicago: William H. Wise & Co., 1916.

Humphrey, William D. *Findlay, The Story of a Community.* Findlay, Ohio: Findlay Printing and Supply Co., 1961.

Hyde, A. M. "The Measure of His Stature." *Commons* 9 (1904):360-361.

"In the Public Eye." *Munsey's Magazine* 25 (1901):329-338.

"Is the Golden Rule Practicable?" *The Outlook* 93 (1909):534-535.

Johnson, Wendell F. *Toledo's Non-Partisan Movement.* Toledo, Ohio: H. J. Chittenden Co. Press, 1922.

Kaptur, Marcia Carolyn. "Unorthodox 'Golden Rule' Jones: Crusader and Scientific Reformer." Honors paper, University of Wisconsin, 1968.

Klein, Maury and Harvey A. Kantor. *Prisoners of Progress: American Industrial Cities, 1850-1920.* New York: Macmillan Publishing Company, 1976.

"The Late Mayor Jones." *The Independent* 52 (1904):162-163.

"The Late Mayor Jones: His Life and Ideals." *The Arena* 32 (1904):323-324.

"The Late Samuel M. Jones: 'Golden Rule' Mayor of Toledo." *Charities and The Commons* 17 (1906):176.

"The Man Without a Party." *The Outlook* 74 (1903):73.

"Mayor Jones and Mr. Dooley." *Toledo Critic* 12 (April 11, 1903)

McLoughlin, William G. "Jones vs. Jones." *American Heritage*, April 1, 1961, p. 56.

McLoughlin, William G., Jr. *Modern Revivalism: Charles Grandison Finney to Billy Graham*. New York: Ronald Press Co., 1959.

McQuaid, Kim. "The Businessman as Reformer: Nelson O. Nelson and Late 19th Century Social Movements in America." *The American Journal of Economics and Sociology* 33 (1974):423-435.

_____. "Samuel Milton Jones: Government and the Golden Rule in Toledo, 1897-1904." *Ohioana Quarterly* 16 (1973):128-130.

Men of Northwestern Ohio. Bowling Green and Toledo, Ohio: C. S. Van Tassel, Publisher, 1898.

Merrell, John B. "Samuel M. Jones: The Mayor." *Commons* 9 (1904):351-355.

The 1976 History of Allen County, Ohio. Edited by John R. Carnes. Evanston, Ind.: Unigraphic, 1976.

Norton, William J. "Chief Kohler of Cleveland and his Golden Rule Policy." *The Outlook* 93 (1909):534.

Nye, Russel B. *Midwestern Progressive Politics: A Historical Study of Its Origins and Development, 1870-1958*. New York, Evanston and London: Harper and Row, Harper Torchbooks, 1965.

Pearson, George W. *The Transition: A Tale of Northwestern Ohio*. Van Wert, Ohio: Wilkinson Printing Co., 1953.

The Philistine. 12 (April 1901):143; 17 (October 1903):156-157.

Pitzer, Donald E. "Revivalism and Politics in Toledo: 1899." *Northwest Ohio Quarterly* 41 (Winter 1968-69):13-24.

Pomeroy, Eltweed. "Samuel M. Jones - An Appreciation." *American Fabian* 4 (July 1898):1-3.

"The Progress of the World: Mayor Jones of Toledo and the Significance of the Toledo Election." *The American Monthly Review of Reviews* 19 (1899): 520-521.

"The Progress of the World: Municipal Tendencies." *The American Monthly Review of Reviews* 27 (1903):532-533.

Reuling, William J. "Samuel 'Golden Rule' Jones and the City-Family Ideal." Mimeographed. Toledo, Ohio: University of Toledo, 1971.

A Review of Toledo's Industries, Her Manufacturers and Merchants. Edited by Thomas K. Bates. Toledo, Ohio: Business Men's Chamber of Commerce Co., 1905.

Reynolds, Minnie J. "The Golden-Rule Mayor." *The Designer*. April 1911, p. 398.

Roberts, T. R. *Eminent Welshmen: A Short Biographical Dictionary of Welshmen Who Have Attained Distinction From the Earliest Times to the Present*. vol. 1. Cardiff and Merthyr Tydfil: Educational Publishing Co., Ltd., 1908.

Rodabaugh, James H. "Samuel M. Jones - Evangel of Equality." *The Historical Society of Northwestern Ohio Quarterly Bulletin* 15 (1943):17-46.

"Samuel Milton Jones." *Commons* 9 (1904):344-348.

"Samuel M. Jones." *Municipal Affairs* 3 (1899):573.

"Samuel Milton Jones: The Golden Rule Mayor by One Who Knew Him." *The Arena* 35 (1906):126-132.

Saulsbury, Elwood. "Samuel M. Jones: Golden Rule Mayor of Toledo." *Frank Leslie's Popular Monthly* 53 (1902):642-647.

Selected Writings of Elbert Hubbard. Memorial ed. vol. 4. East Aurora, N.Y.: The Roycrofters, and New York: William H. Wise & Co., 1928.

"Social Ideals and Idealists." *The Arena* 32 (1904):323-325.

The State of Ohio *ex rel*. Kniseley *et al*. v. Jones *et al*., 66 Ohio State 453 (1902)

Stinchcombe, Jean L. *Reform and Reaction: City Politics in Toledo*. Belmont, Calif.: Wadsworth Publishing Co., 1968.

Tager, Jack. *The Intellectual as Urban Reformer: Brand Whitlock and the Progressive Movement*. Cleveland: Case Western Reserve University Press, 1968.

_____. "Progressives, Conservatives, and the Theory of the Status Revolution." *Mid-America* 48 (July 1966):162-175.

Tanner, Allan A. "The Measure of His Stature." *Commons* 9 (1904):360.

_____. "Samuel M. Jones as an Employer." *Commons* 9 (1904):357-358.

Taylor, Graham. "Golden Rule Jones' Own Day." *Commons* 9 (1904):348-350.

Toledo Critic. 7 (April 3, 1897)

Traubel, Horace. "Jones of Toledo." *Conservator*, August 1902, p. 88.

"Two Notable Reform Victories in Ohio." *The Arena* 29 (1903):651-655.

U.S. Congress, House. Employee-Employer Relations. 75th Congress, 3rd session, 1938. *Congressional Record*, 83, pt. 9:951-953.

Waggoner, Clark, Collection of Scrapbooks and Letterbooks, Local History Department, Toledo-Lucas County Public Library.

Warner, Hoyt Landon. *Progressivism in Ohio, 1897-1917*. Columbus, Ohio: Ohio State University Press, 1964.

Warner, Mason and J. Hazard Perry. *The Lincoln Club*. Toledo, Ohio: Warner and Perry, 1899.

"What Should the City Own?" *The American Monthly Review of Reviews* 18 (1898): 462-463.

"Whimsies." *The Whim* 4 (1903):165-175.

Whitlock, Brand. "Backing Up an Independent Mayor." *Charities and the Commons* 17 (1906-07):240-242.

_____. "Campaigning with 'Sam Jones'." *Commons* 9 (1904):355-356.

_____. "Forty Years of It." *American Magazine* 75 (April 1913):49-54; 75 (May 1913):47-52; 75 (June 1913):44-49.

_____. *Forty Years of It*. New York and London: D. Appleton and Co., 1930.

_____. "Golden Rule Jones." In *A Treaty Never Broken & Other Stories*, by Ernest E. Taylor, pp. 22-28. London: Society of Friends, 1925.

_____. "'Golden Rule' Jones." *World's Work* 8 (1904):5308-5311.

_____. "The Measure of His Stature." *Commons* 9 (1904):361-362.

Woodruff, Clinton R. "Municipal Government in Ohio." *Yale Review* 12 (August 1903):121-240.

PAMPHLETS

Ferguson, Charles. *The Toledo of Jones*. Toledo, Ohio: Schmit and Anzenbacher, Printers, n.d.

The Golden Rule Apostle: Mayor Jones of Toledo. [Cincinnati?, n.d.]

Mr. Jones and His Theories. [Akron: Allied Printing Trades Council, 1899.]

Mowry, George E. *The Progressive Era, 1900-20: The Reform Persuasion*. Washington, D.C.: American Historical Association, 1972.

Non-Partisan Candidate for Governor, by R. L. M. Toledo, Ohio: Hadley Printing Co., [1899.]

Wisner, Edward. *Mayor Jones and Public Ownership*. [Cleveland, Ohio: Allied Printing Trades Council, 1899.]

TAPE RECORDINGS

Downes, Randolph C. "Famous Northwest Ohioans: Samuel M. Jones, (1846-1904) 'Golden Rule' Mayor." Toledo, Ohio: WSPD-TV, April 12, 1959.

"Samuel M. 'Golden Rule' Jones Family History: A Conversation with Descendants." Toledo, Ohio: Jean W. Strong, June 5, 1976.

NEWSPAPERS

In addition to the Toledo newspapers, researchers should consult the major Ohio and national newspapers of the period for coverage of the mayor's activities.